Introduction

Pupils' written work

Abacus textbooks are unique in that they provide clear guidance to pupils on how their work should be recorded. Pupils should be encouraged to follow this guidance, which will make marking their work substantially easier, and clearly focused.

Marking pupils' work

Clearly it is important that pupils' work is seen and checked by the teacher regularly, but it is not necessary for all work to be marked by the teacher. Decisions about which work should be teacher-marked, and how it should be marked will be made alongside the need to maximise time available for teaching and guiding pupils through their activities.

A suggested approach within Abacus is to make these decisions Unit by Unit. Decide, for example, for each Unit, which parts you want to mark, and which parts the pupils can mark.

Marking the 'Explores'

The 'Explores' should generally be marked by the teacher. The 'Explores' often require a systematic approach, and the answers give suggestions for these. These approaches can be communicated to the pupils, to help them develop systematic ways of working. Also, the pupils' responses to the 'Explores' may well vary because of the often open-ended nature of the activities.

For many 'Explores' you may want to ask the pupils to work in pairs or groups, possibly leading to a group display of the results of their 'exploration'.

Contents

Number Textbook 1

page 3

4-digit numbers

1. £3000, £600, £80, £1
2. £6000, £600, £90, £9
3. £1000, £200, £70, £9
4. £1000, £800, £50, £5
5. £4000, £500, £30, £7
6. £4000, £500, £7
7. £2000, £10, £6
8. £7000, £100, £10
9. £3000, £800, £5

Numbers in order £1279 £1855 £2016 £3681 £3805 £4507 £4537 £6699 £7110

10. 2764
11. 4229
12. 5993
13. 8644
14. 1117
15. 5082
16. 7960
17. 1406
18. 4720

Numbers in order 1117 1406 2764 4229 4720 5082 5993 7960 8644

● 1117 1279 1406 1855 2016 2764 3681 3805 4229
4507 4537 4720 5082 5993 6699 7110 7960 8644

---

page 4

4-digit numbers

1. 700
2. 500
3. 70
4. 4000
5. 600
6. 9
7. 2000
8. 70
9. 900
10. 1

Train numbers in order 2803 3772 3972 4013 4768 6690 6960 7241 8561 9999

● Answers will vary.

Explore

11. 2003, 2005, 2060, 2063, 2065, 2090, 2093, 2095, 2100, 2103, 2105, 2160, 2163, 2165, 2190, 2193, 2195
12. 2700, 2703, 2705, 2760, 2763, 2765, 2790, 2793, 2795
13. 3003, 3005, 3060, 3063, 3065, 3090, 3093, 3095, 3100, 3103, 3105, 3160, 3163, 3165, 3190, 3193, 3195
14. 3700, 3703, 3705, 3760, 3763, 3765, 3790, 3793, 3795

Number Textbook 1

page 5
4-digit numbers

Place-value N1

1. 1213 < 1867   Blues won by 654 points
2. 1975 > 1933   Reds won by 42 points
3. 2410 > 2230   Reds won by 180 points
4. 3014 < 3118   Blues won by 104 points
5. 3667 < 3676   Blues won by 9 points
6. 4110 > 4100   Reds won by 10 points
7. 5568 < 5881   Blues won by 313 points
8. 6314 > 5999   Reds won by 315 points
9. 8006 < 8600   Blues won by 594 points

☺ See answers above.

10. 3890 > 3880
11. 4230 > 4130 (or 4030)
12. 3156 < 3166 (or 3176, 3186, 3196)
13. 2899 < 2903 (or 2913, 2923, 2933, 2943, 2953, 2963, 2973, 2983, 2993)
14. 3052 > 3042 (or 3032, 3022, 3012, 3002)
15. 4548 < 4549, 4640 (or 4641, ... 4649), 4740 (or 4741, ... 4749), 4840 (or 4841, ... 4849), 4940 (or 4941, ... 4949)
16. (8309, 8319, 8329, 8339 or) 8349 < 8350 (or 8351, 8352, 8353, 8354, 8355, 8356, 8357, 8358, 8359)

page 6
4-digit numbers

Place-value N1

1. 4392   2. 1584   3. 5136   4. 8744   5. 9220
6. 3500   7. 2890   8. 6030

Numbers in order   1584   2890   3500   4392   5136   6030   8744   9220

9. Five thousand, two hundred and seventy-one miles
10. Eight thousand, three hundred and forty-three miles
11. Two thousand, five hundred and seventy miles
12. Six thousand, six hundred and ninety-four miles
13. Five thousand, one hundred and forty miles
14. Two thousand, six hundred and three miles
15. Three thousand, three hundred and seventeen miles

☺ 9. 5281 miles   10. 8353 miles   11. 2580 miles   12. 6704 miles
13. 5150 miles   14. 2613 miles   15. 3327 miles

Number Textbook 1

Adding to 10

1. $8 + 2 = 10$
2. $4 + 6 = 10$
3. $9 + 1 = 10$
4. $3 + 7 = 10$
5. $0 + 10 = 10$
6. $4 + 6 = 10$
7. $5 + 5 = 10$
8. $7 + 3 = 10$
9. $1 + 9 = 10$
10. $2 + 8 = 10$

11. $8p + 12p = 20p$
12. $5p + 15p = 20p$
13. $4p + 16p = 20p$
14. $1p + 19p = 20p$
15. $7p + 13p = 20p$
16. $2p + 18p = 20p$
17. $6p + 14p = 20p$

Explore
Answers will vary.

Adding to the next ten

1. $28 + 2 = 30$
2. $42 + 8 = 50$
3. $54 + 6 = 60$
4. $17 + 3 = 20$
5. $11 + 9 = 20$
6. $75 + 5 = 80$
7. $66 + 4 = 70$
8. $83 + 7 = 90$
9. $59 + 1 = 60$

10. $43 + 7 = 50$
11. $66 + 4 = 70$
12. $5 + 15 = 20$
13. $38 + 2 = 40$
14. $8 + 92 = 100$
15. $54 + 6 = 60$
16. $3 + 27 = 30$
17. $5 + 75 = 80$
18. $61 + 9 = 70$
19. $41 + 9 = 50$

Adding to the next ten

1. £24 + £6 = £30, £6 more
2. £42 + £8 = £50, £8 more
3. £58 + £2 = £60, £2 more
4. £17 + £3 = £20, £3 more
5. £73 + £7 = £80, £7 more
6. £36 + £4 = £40, £4 more
7. £45 + £5 = £50, £5 more
8. £63 + £7 = £70, £7 more
9. £94 + £6 = £100, £6 more
10. £88 + £2 = £90, £2 more
11. £29 + £1 = £30, £1 more
12. £51 + £9 = £60, £9 more

13. Jane: $63 + 7 = 70$ she must borrow 7p
14. Timo: $74 - 12 = 62$ $62 + 8 = 70$ he must save 8p
15. Matthew: $73 + 7 = 80$ song was 7 minutes long

Number Textbook 1

Finding the difference

  1. $135 - 128 = 7$ **2.** $234 - 226 = 8$ **3.** $181 - 173 = 8$
  4. $163 - 157 = 6$ **5.** $305 - 299 = 6$ **6.** $501 - 492 = 9$

$92 - 76 = 16$ cm	up 16 cm from Monday to Tuesday
$104 - 92 = 12$ cm	up 12 cm from Tuesday to Wednesday
$110 - 104 = 6$ cm	up 6 cm from Wednesday to Thursday
$111 - 110 = 1$ cm	up 1 cm from Thursday to Friday
$122 - 111 = 11$ cm	up 11 cm from Friday to Saturday
$134 - 122 = 12$ cm	up 12 cm from Saturday to Sunday

Finding the difference

  1. $226 - 217 = 9$ **2.** $184 - 178 = 6$ **3.** $232 - 226 = 6$
  4. $151 - 144 = 7$ **5.** $253 - 247 = 6$ **6.** $333 - 326 = 7$
  7. $125 - 116 = 9$

🖉   Answers will vary.

Shahid	$130 - 122 = 8$	Jane	$140 - 136 = 4$
Tim	$140 - 133 = 7$	Jobe	$150 - 142 = 8$
Yasmin	$150 - 141 = 9$	Mel	$150 - 146 = 4$

Finding the difference

  1. $136 - 128 = 8$ **2.** $223 - 215 = 8$ **3.** $243 - 237 = 6$
  4. $355 - 348 = 7$ **5.** $192 - 188 = 4$ **6.** $273 - 266 = 7$
  7. $383 - 376 = 7$ **8.** $452 - 447 = 5$ **9.** $333 - 325 = 8$

10. $123 + 8 = 131$ $131 - 125 = 6$ 6 stickers left
11. $240 - 224 = 16$ 16 stickers

Number Textbook 1

Adding pairs to 100 and 1000

Table 1
Pairs to 100

0 + 100 = 100	55 + 45 = 100
5 + 95 = 100	60 + 40 = 100
10 + 90 = 100	65 + 35 = 100
15 + 85 = 100	70 + 30 = 100
20 + 80 = 100	75 + 25 = 100
25 + 75 = 100	80 + 20 = 100
30 + 70 = 100	85 + 15 = 100
35 + 65 = 100	90 + 10 = 100
40 + 60 = 100	95 + 5 = 100
45 + 55 = 100	100 + 0 = 100
50 + 50 = 100	

Table 2
Pairs to 1000

0 + 1000 = 1000	550 + 450 = 1000
50 + 950 = 1000	600 + 400 = 1000
100 + 900 = 1000	650 + 350 = 1000
150 + 850 = 1000	700 + 300 = 1000
200 + 800 = 1000	750 + 250 = 1000
250 + 750 = 1000	800 + 200 = 1000
300 + 700 = 1000	850 + 150 = 1000
350 + 650 = 1000	900 + 100 = 1000
400 + 600 = 1000	950 + 50 = 1000
450 + 550 = 1000	1000 + 0 = 1000
500 + 500 = 1000	

The numbers in Table 2 are all 10 times the numbers in Table 1.

a 45, 55	**b** 95, 5	**c** 40, 60	**d** 35, 65	**e** 75, 25
f 15, 85	**g** 20, 80	**h** 10, 90	**i** 65, 35	**j** 85, 15
k 70, 30	**l** 55, 45			

Number Textbook 1

Adding pairs to 100 and 1000

1. $350 + 650 = 1000$ ml
2. $250 + 750 = 1000$ ml
3. $150 + 850 = 1000$ ml
4. $550 + 450 = 1000$ ml
5. $400 + 600 = 1000$ ml
6. $650 + 350 = 1000$ ml
7. $200 + 800 = 1000$ ml
8. $450 + 550 = 1000$ ml

9. £85   10. £45   11. £64   12. £28   13. £81

Adding pairs to 100

$60 + 40 = 100$ kg $68 + 32 = 100$ kg $55 + 45 = 100$ kg

$26 + 74 = 100$ kg $49 + 51 = 100$ kg

Explore

Any of the following:

13, 87	14, 86	16, 84	17, 83	21, 79	24, 76	26, 74
29, 71	31, 69	32, 68	38, 62	39, 61	41, 59	42, 58
43, 57	47, 53	48, 52	49, 51			

Adding several numbers

1. $£7 + £3 + £11 + £8 = £29$
2. $£8 + £8 + £3 + £12 = £31$
3. $£13 + £13 + £7 + £7 + £9 = £49$
4. $£13 + £7 + £4 + £4 = £28$
5. $£12 + £2 + £6 + £13 = £33$
6. $£6 + £6 + £2 + £2 + £4 = £20$
7. $£11 + £7 + £3 + £9 = £30$
8. $£11 + £6 + £9 + £3 = £29$
9. $£3 + £3 + £12 + £2 + £2 + £8 = £30$
10. $£7 + £7 + £8 + £6 = £28$

@ Answers will vary.

11. $4 + 7 + 8 + 9 = 28$
12. $8 + 6 + 5 + 4 = 23$
13. $6 + 12 + 6 + 7 = 31$
14. $13 + 9 + 7 + 8 = 37$
15. $11 + 8 + 9 + 12 = 40$
16. $4 + 8 + 6 + 2 + 9 = 29$
17. $13 + 11 + 9 + 7 = 40$
18. $15 + 3 + 5 + 8 + 7 = 38$

Number Textbook 1

Adding several numbers

1. $6 + 4 + 8 + 5 + 3 = 26$
2. $9 + 2 + 4 + 8 = 23$
3. $5 + 9 + 6 + 8 = 28$
4. $3 + 7 + 9 + 2 + 4 = 25$
5. $3 + 5 + 8 + 12 = 28$
6. $3 + 5 + 7 + 11 + 8 = 34$
7. $5 + 9 + 6 + 8 + 12 = 40$
8. $3 + 7 + 11 + 2 + 8 = 31$

9. Answers will vary.

Adding several numbers

1. $5 + 3 + 4 + 9 + 8 = 29$
2. $10 + 5 + 3 + 8 + 7 = 33$
3. $6 + 9 + 8 + 4 + 9 = 36$
4. $7 + 9 + 11 + 3 + 8 = 38$
5. $9 + 8 + 9 + 2 + 8 = 36$
6. $9 + 6 + 8 + 5 + 8 = 36$
7. $5 + 3 + 14 + 5 + 6 = 33$
8. $4 + 7 + 12 + 9 + 8 = 40$
9. $9 + 11 + 9 + 6 + 6 = 41$

Explore

$2 + 8 + 9 = 19$, $2 + 8 + 3 + 6 = 19$, $2 + 8 + 4 + 5 = 19$, $3 + 7 + 9 = 19$,
$3 + 7 + 4 + 5 = 19$, $4 + 6 + 9 = 19$, $4 + 6 + 2 + 7 = 19$, $4 + 7 + 8 = 19$,
$5 + 6 + 8 = 19$, $2 + 3 + 5 + 9 = 19$

Adding several numbers

1. $12 + 9 + 7 + 8 + 7 = 43$
2. $11 + 10 + 8 + 7 + 6 = 42$
3. $6 + 4 + 9 + 10 + 10 = 39$
4. $3 + 3 + 8 + 5 + 9 = 28$
5. $8 + 4 + 2 + 8 + 7 = 29$
6. $6 + 11 + 10 + 4 + 3 = 34$
7. $7 + 7 + 14 + 10 + 7 = 45$
8. $5 + 4 + 10 + 11 + 9 = 39$

Cost of names: answers will vary.

e   Answers will vary.

Number Textbook 1

Counting in 1s, 25s and 50s

1. 347, 348, 349	**2.** 228, 229, 230	**3.** 409, 410, 411
4. 666, 667, 668	**5.** 398, 399, 400	**6.** 800, 801, 802
7. 849, 850, 851	**8.** 309, 310, 311	**9.** 99, 100, 101
10. 554, 555, 556	**11.** 737, 738, 739	**12.** 915, 916, 917

◉ **1.** 338, 348, 358	**2.** 219, 229, 239	**3.** 400, 410, 420
4. 657, 667, 677	**5.** 389, 399, 409	**6.** 791, 801, 811
7. 840, 850, 860	**8.** 300, 310, 320	**9.** 90, 100, 110
10. 545, 555, 565	**11.** 728, 738, 748	**12.** 906, 916, 926

13. 200, 250, 300	**14.** 175, 200, 225	**15.** 375, 400, 425
16. 250, 275, 300	**17.** 750, 800, 850	**18.** 1050, 1100, 1150

Counting in 25s and 50s

1. £4·50 + 50p = £5·00	**2.** 30p + 50p = 80p
3. £1·10 + 50p = £1·60	**4.** £2·20 + 50p = £2·70
5. £3·40 + 50p = £3·90	**6.** £6·50 + 50p = £7·00
7. £2·00 + 50p = £2·50	**8.** £5·20 + 50p = £5·70
9. £7·00 + 50p = £7·50	**10.** £4·40 + 50p = £4·90
11. £9·30 + 50p = £9·80	**12.** £8·50 + 50p = £9·00
13. £7·10 + 50p = £7·60	

14. 600, 550, 500	**15.** 225, 200, 175	**16.** 825, 800, 175
17. 850, 800, 750	**18.** 500, 450, 400	**19.** 275, 250, 225

Counting in 25s and 50s

1. 763, 813, 863, 913
2. 192, 242, 292, 342, 392, 442, 492
3. 518, 568, 618, 668, 718, 768, 818
4. 360, 310, 260, 210, 160, 110, 60
5. 474, 524, 574, 624, 674, 724, 774
6. 1180, 1130, 1080, 1030, 980, 930, 880

Explore

0 to 1000 in 25s: would write 20 numbers ending in 5
1000 to 2000 in 25s: would write 20 numbers ending in 5

Number Textbook 1

Multiplying

  I. $2 \times 4 = 8$ **2.** $3 \times 2 = 6$ **3** $4 \times 4 = 16$ **4.** $3 \times 3 = 9$

Neil and Ella	$4 \times 5 = 5 \times 4$
Kate and Jane	$2 \times 6 = 6 \times 2$
Bec and Amos	$3 \times 5 = 5 \times 3$
Mike and Carlos	$2 \times 8 = 8 \times 2$
Habeeb and Samira	$3 \times 6 = 6 \times 3$
Jo and Bob	$4 \times 6 = 6 \times 4$

Multiplying

  I. $2 \times 5 = 10, 5 \times 2 = 10$ **2.** $3 \times 5 = 15, 5 \times 3 = 15$
  3. $3 \times 7 = 21, 7 \times 3 = 21$ **4.** $4 \times 2 = 8, 2 \times 4 = 8$

  5. $2 \times 9 = 18, 9 \times 2 = 18$ and $3 \times 6 = 18, 6 \times 3 = 18$
  6. $2 \times 6 = 12, 6 \times 2 = 12$ and $4 \times 3 = 12, 3 \times 4 = 12$
  7. $2 \times 12 = 24, 12 \times 2 = 24$ and $3 \times 8 = 24, 8 \times 3 = 24$
      (or $4 \times 6 = 24, 6 \times 4 = 24$)
  8. $2 \times 8 = 16, 8 \times 2 = 16$ and $4 \times 4 = 16$

9. $8 \times 2 = 16$	$2 \times 8 = 16$	**10.** $3 \times 4 = 12$	$4 \times 3 = 12$
II. $2 \times 5 = 10$	$5 \times 2 = 10$	**12.** $6 \times 3 = 18$	$3 \times 6 = 18$
13. $3 \times 10 = 30$	$10 \times 3 = 30$	**14.** $7 \times 2 = 14$	$2 \times 7 = 14$
15. $9 \times 5 = 45$	$5 \times 9 = 45$	**16.** $1 \times 6 = 6$	$6 \times 1 = 6$
17. $8 \times 3 = 24$	$3 \times 8 = 24$	**18.** $9 \times 2 = 18$	$2 \times 9 = 18$
19. $5 \times 4 = 20$	$4 \times 5 = 20$	**20.** $6 \times 4 = 24$	$4 \times 6 = 24$

Multiplying

  I. $4 \times 45p = 180p = £1 \cdot 80$ **2.** $2 \times 55p = 110p = £1 \cdot 10$
  3. $3 \times 60p = 180p = £1 \cdot 80$ **4.** $3 \times 45p = 135p = £1 \cdot 35$
  5. $4 \times 35p = 140p = £1 \cdot 40$ **6.** $5 \times 45p = 225p = £2 \cdot 25$
  7. $3 \times 55p = 165p = £1 \cdot 65$ **8.** $5 \times 60p = 300p = £3 \cdot 00$
  9. $4 \times 55p = 220p = £2 \cdot 20$

Screamer	11 turns ($£4 \cdot 95$)
Dipper	9 turns ($£4 \cdot 95$)
Big Wish	8 turns ($£4 \cdot 80$)
Water Splash	14 turns ($£4 \cdot 90$)

Number Textbook 1

Explore

24: 1 x 24 = 24, 24 x 1 = 24
     2 x 12 = 24, 12 x 2 = 24
     3 x 8 = 24, 8 x 3 = 24
     4 x 6 = 24, 6 x 4 = 24   4 pairs

18: 1 x 18 = 18, 18 x 1 = 18
     2 x 9 = 18, 9 x 2 = 18
     3 x 6 = 18, 6 x 3 = 18   3 pairs

60: 1 x 60 = 60, 60 x 1 = 60
     2 x 30 = 60, 30 x 2 = 60
     3 x 20 = 60, 20 x 3 = 60
     4 x 15 = 60, 15 x 4 = 60
     5 x 12 = 60, 12 x 5 = 60
     6 x 10 = 60, 10 x 6 = 60   6 pairs

Multiplying

1. 20 x 3 m = 3 m x 20 = 60 m
2. 30 x 2 m = 2 m x 30 = 60 m
3. 31 x 5 m = 5 m x 31 = 155 m
4. 25 x 6 m = 6 m x 25 = 150 m
5. 38 x $\frac{1}{2}$ m = $\frac{1}{2}$ m x 38 = 19 m
6. 35 x 4 m = 4 m x 35 = 140 m

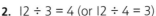 1. 120 m 2. 80 m 3. 200 m 4. 240 m 5. 20 m 6. 160 m

7. 4 x 60p = 240p = £2·40 £2·40 – £2·00 = 40p needs 40p more
8. 3 x 40p = 120p = £1·20 2 x 50p = 100p = £1·00
   £1·20 + £1·00 = £2·20 total cost £2·20
9. 5 x 40 cm = 200 cm 3 m = 300 cm 300 cm – 200 cm = 100 cm 1 m left
10. 5 x 30p = 150p = £1·50 £2·00 – £1·50 = 50p 50p change

Dividing

1. 18 ÷ 3 = 6 (or 18 ÷ 6 = 3)
2. 12 ÷ 3 = 4 (or 12 ÷ 4 = 3)
3. 16 ÷ 2 = 8 (or 16 ÷ 8 = 2)
4. 15 ÷ 5 = 3 (or 15 ÷ 3 = 5)
5. 28 ÷ 4 = 7 (or 28 ÷ 7 = 4)
6. 30 ÷ 5 = 6 (or 30 ÷ 6 = 5)
7. 40 ÷ 5 = 8 (or 40 ÷ 8 = 5)
8. 21 ÷ 3 = 7 (or 21 ÷ 7 = 3)
9. 12 ÷ 4 = 3 (or 12 ÷ 3 = 4)
10. 27 ÷ 3 = 9 (or 27 ÷ 9 = 3)

11. 20 ÷ 4 = 5
12. 30 ÷ 3 = 10
13. 14 ÷ 2 = 7
14. 16 ÷ 4 = 4
15. 28 ÷ 7 = 4
16. 18 ÷ 2 = 9
17. 16 ÷ 2 = 8
18. 12 ÷ 6 = 2
19. 20 ÷ 5 = 4
20. 30 ÷ 10 = 3
21. 25 ÷ 5 = 5
22. 24 ÷ 6 = 4

Number Textbook 1

Dividing

1. $18 \div 3 = 6$
2. $30 \div 3 = 10$
3. $15 \div 3 = 5$
4. $24 \div 3 = 8$
5. $21 \div 3 = 7$
6. $33 \div 3 = 11$
7. $36 \div 3 = 12$
8. $27 \div 3 = 9$
9. $39 \div 3 = 13$

10. $25 \div 5 = 5$
11. $40 \div 5 = 8$
12. $24 \div 4 = 6$
13. $28 \div 4 = 7$
14. $30 \div 10 = 3$
15. $60 \div 6 = 10$
16. $14 \div 2 = 7$
17. $60 \div 5 = 12$
18. $24 \div 3 = 8$
19. $36 \div 4 = 9$
20. $27 \div 3 = 9$

Dividing

1. $20 \div 4 = 5$
2. $32 \div 4 = 8$
3. $40 \div 4 = 10$
4. $28 \div 4 = 7$
5. $16 \div 4 = 4$
6. $48 \div 4 = 12$

7. $40 \div 5 = 8$
8. $90 \div 10 = 9$
9. $10 \div 2 = 5$
10. $16 \div 4 = 4$
11. $20 \div 5 = 4$
12. $21 \div 3 = 7$
13. $24 \div 6 = 4$
14. $30 \div 5 = 6$
15. $36 \div 6 = 6$
16. $24 \div 2 = 12$

Explore

$36 \div 1 = 36$ $36 \div 2 = 18$ $36 \div 3 = 12$ $36 \div 4 = 9$ $36 \div 6 = 6$
$36 \div 9 = 4$ $36 \div 12 = 3$ $36 \div 18 = 2$ $36 \div 36 = 1$
9 pairs

Dividing

1. $35 \text{ cm} \div 5 = 7 \text{ cm}$
2. $27 \text{ cm} \div 3 = 9 \text{ cm}$
3. $44 \text{ cm} \div 2 = 22 \text{ cm}$
4. $36 \text{ cm} \div 6 = 6 \text{ cm}$
5. $32 \text{ cm} \div 4 = 8 \text{ cm}$
6. $66 \text{ cm} \div 2 = 33 \text{ cm}$
7. $110 \text{ cm} \div 10 = 11 \text{ cm}$
8. $21 \text{ cm} \div 3 = 7 \text{ cm}$
9. $45 \text{ cm} \div 5 = 9 \text{ cm}$
10. $54 \text{ cm} \div 6 = 9 \text{ cm}$

🌐 Total of 46 pieces

11. $24 \div 4 = 6$ 6 cats
12. $3 \times 9 = 27$ $27 + 2 = 29$ 29 biscuits
13. $40 \div 5 = 8$ 8 piles
14. $£36 \div 4 = £9$ £9 each
    $4 \times £10 = £40$ $£40 - £36 = £4$ need £4 more

Number Textbook 1

page 31
Multiplying

1. a 6   b 16
2. c 15   d 35
3. e 8   f 16   g 36
4. h 30   i 60
5. j 12   k 18   l 27

6. $3 \times 4 = 12$
7. $2 \times 5 = 10$
8. $4 \times 10 = 40$
9. $6 \times 3 = 18$
10. $4 \times 4 = 16$
11. $3 \times 3 = 9$
12. $8 \times 5 = 40$
13. $9 \times 3 = 27$
14. $8 \times 2 = 16$
15. $7 \times 4 = 28$
16. $5 \times 2 = 10$
17. $10 \times 5 = 50$
18. $7 \times 3 = 21$

---

page 32
Multiplying and dividing

1. 8, 12, 16, 24, 28, 32, 36, 40
2. 9, 12, 15, 18, 21, 24, 27, 30, 36, 42
3. 12, 24, 36
4. 14, 22

5. $8 \div 2 = 4$
6. $12 \div 3 = 4$
7. $5 \times 4 = 20$
8. $40 \div 10 = 4$
9. $25 \div 5 = 5$
10. $7 \times 5 = 35$
11. $32 \div 4 = 8$
12. $9 \times 3 = 27$
13. $18 \div 2 = 9$
14. $21 \div 3 = 7$

---

page 33
Multiplying and dividing

1. $4 \times 4 = 16$
2. $18 \div 3 = 6$
3. $5 \times 4 = 20$
4. $7 \times 3 = 21$
5. $20 \div 4 = 5$
6. $9 \times 3 = 27$
7. $28 \div 4 = 7$
8. $8 \times 3 = 24$
9. $35 \div 5 = 7$
10. $3 \times 4 = 12$

11. 6, 12, 18, 24, 30, 36, 42, 48, 54, 60
12. 12, 24, 36, 48, 60
13. 15, 30, 45, 60
14. 20, 40, 60
15. 30, 60
16. 10, 20, 30, 40, 50, 60
17. 20, 40, 60
18. 4, 8, 12, 16, 20, 24, 28, 32, 36, 40, 44, 48, 52, 56, 60

℮ Answers will vary.

Number Textbook 1

Doubling and halving

1. double 18 = 20 + 16 = 36
2. double 37 = 60 + 14 = 74
3. double 48 = 80 + 16 = 96
4. double 26 = 40 + 12 = 52
5. double 29 = 40 + 18 = 58
6. double 46 = 80 + 12 = 92
7. double 27 = 40 + 14 = 54
8. double 57 = 100 + 14 = 114
9. double 38 = 60 + 16 = 76
10. double 36 = 60 + 12 = 72

11. half of 12 = 6
12. half of 16 = 8
13. half of 20 = 10
14. half of 30 = 15
15. half of 18 = 9
16. half of 24 = 12
17. half of 42 = 21
18. half of 64 = 32
19. half of 32 = 16
20. half of 80 = 40
21. half of 60 = 30
22. half of 48 = 24
23. half of 88 = 44

@ 11. 3 12. 4 13. 5 14. $7\frac{1}{2}$ 15. $4\frac{1}{2}$ 16. 6 17. $10\frac{1}{2}$ 18. 16 19. 8
20. 20 21. 15 22. 12 23. 22

Doubling

1. 2 x 23p = 46p
2. 2 x 42p = 84p
3. 2 x 31p = 62p
4. 2 x 18p = 36p
5. 2 x 25p = 50p
6. 2 x 13p = 26p
7. 2 x 35p = 70p
8. 2 x 47p = 94p
9. 2 x 28p = 56p
10. 2 x 22p = 44p
11. 2 x 33p = 66p
12. 2 x 29p = 58p
13. 2 x 44p = 88p

14.

in	20	50	70	90	60	30	80	40
out	40	100	140	180	120	60	160	80

15.

in	15	55	75	45	25	85	35	65
out	30	110	150	90	50	170	70	130

Number Textbook 1

Doubling and halving

1. double 23 + 24 = 46 + 24 = 70
2. double 25 + 28 = 50 + 28 = 78
3. 26 + double 21 = 26 + 42 = 68
4. double 26 + double 24 = 52 + 48 = 100
5. double 34 + 31 = 68 + 31 = 99
6. 32 + double 33 = 32 + 66 = 98
7. 39 + double 33 = 39 + 66 = 105
8. 27 + double 43 = 27 + 86 = 113
9. double 34 + 42 = 68 + 42 = 110
10. double 26 + double 43 = 52 + 86 = 138

◉ first board: double 28 + double 28 = 56 + 56 = 112
   second board: double 39 + double 39 = 78 + 78 = 156
   third board: double 43 + double 43 = 86 + 86 = 172

Explore
23 pairs, using each card only once

96, 48	92, 46	90, 45	86, 43	82, 41	78, 39
76, 38	72, 36	70, 35	68, 34	64, 32	62, 31
58, 29	56, 28	54, 27	46, 23	38, 19	36, 18
34, 17	32, 16	30, 15	28, 14	26, 13	

Fours and eights

	x4	x8	◉ (x16)
1.	2 x 4 = 8	2 x 8 = 16	2 x 16 = 32
2.	3 x 4 = 12	3 x 8 = 24	3 x 16 = 48
3.	4 x 4 = 16	4 x 8 = 32	4 x 16 = 64
4.	5 x 4 = 20	5 x 8 = 40	5 x 16 = 80
5.	6 x 4 = 24	6 x 8 = 48	6 x 16 = 96
6.	7 x 4 = 28	7 x 8 = 56	7 x 16 = 112

1. 3 x 8 = 24   2. 2 x 8 = 16   3. 5 x 8 = 40   4. 4 x 8 = 32
5. 1 x 8 = 8   6. 10 x 8 = 80   7. 8 x 8 = 64   8. 6 x 8 = 48
9. 9 x 8 = 72

◉ 1. 12   2. 8   3. 20   4. 16   5. 4   6. 40   7. 32   8. 24   9. 36

Number Textbook 1

Fours and eights

1. 8, 12, 16, 20, 24, 28, 32, 36, 40
2. 8, 16, 24, 32, 40
3. 8, 16, 24, 32, 40
4. 14, 18, 22, 26, 30

@ Answers will vary.

5. $24 \div 8 = 3$	**6.** $40 \div 8 = 5$	**7.** $8 \div 8 = 1$	**8.** $48 \div 8 = 6$
9. $16 \div 8 = 2$	**10.** $80 \div 8 = 10$	**11.** $64 \div 8 = 8$	**12.** $32 \div 8 = 4$
13. $56 \div 8 = 7$	**14.** $72 \div 8 = 9$		

Fours and eights

1. double 40 = 80 $10 \times 8 = 80$	**2.** double 24 = 48 $6 \times 8 = 48$
3. double 52 = 104 $13 \times 8 = 104$	**4.** double 60 = 120 $15 \times 8 = 120$
5. double 32 = 64 $8 \times 8 = 64$	**6.** double 48 = 96 $12 \times 8 = 96$
7. double 80 = 160 $20 \times 8 = 160$	**8.** double 44 = 88 $11 \times 8 = 88$
9. double 400 = 800 $100 \times 8 = 800$	**10.** double 36 = 72 $9 \times 8 = 72$
11. double 120 = 240 $30 \times 8 = 240$	**12.** double 200 = 400 $50 \times 8 = 400$

@ Answers will vary.

Explore
Pattern of units digits in x4 table: 4, 8, 2, 6, 0, 4, 8, …
Pattern of units digits in x8 table: 8, 6, 4, 2, 0, 8, …

Fours and eights

1. $3 \times 8p = 24p$	**2.** $5 \times 8p = 40p$	**3.** $7 \times 8p = 56p$	**4.** $10 \times 8p = 80p$
5. $6 \times 8p = 48p$	**6.** $4 \times 8p = 32p$	**7.** $8 \times 8p = 64p$	**8.** $40p \div 8p = 5$
9. $56p \div 8p = 7$	**10.** $24p \div 8p = 3$	**11.** $64p \div 8p = 8$	**12.** $80p \div 8p = 10$

13. $7 \times 8 = 56$ $60 - 56 = 4$ 7 teams, 4 children left over
14. $7 \times 8 = 56$ 56 people
15. $12 \times 8 = 96$ $100 - 96 = 4$ 12 stamps, 4p change
16. $48 \text{ cm} \div 8 = 6 \text{ cm}$ each side 6 cm long

Number Textbook 1

Fractions

1. $\frac{6}{8}$ 2. $\frac{2}{4}$ 3. $\frac{1}{3}$ 4. $\frac{1}{4}$ 5. $\frac{4}{6}$ 6. $\frac{2}{3}$ 7. $\frac{3}{5}$ 8. $\frac{5}{6}$ 9. $\frac{3}{6}$ 10. $\frac{5}{8}$

11. green $\frac{3}{5}$, yellow $\frac{2}{5}$ 12. green $\frac{2}{8}$, yellow $\frac{6}{8}$ 13. green $\frac{5}{9}$, yellow $\frac{4}{9}$

14. green $\frac{2}{6}$, yellow $\frac{4}{6}$ 15. green $\frac{4}{8}$, yellow $\frac{4}{8}$ 16. green $\frac{1}{7}$, yellow $\frac{6}{7}$

17. green $\frac{5}{10}$, yellow $\frac{5}{10}$

Fractions

1. $2\frac{2}{5}$ 2. $1\frac{3}{4}$ 3. $3\frac{1}{2}$ 4. $2\frac{2}{3}$ 5. $1\frac{5}{6}$ 6. $2\frac{3}{8}$ 7. $3\frac{2}{6}$

❷ 1. $2\frac{3}{5}$ 2. $3\frac{1}{4}$ 3. $1\frac{1}{2}$ 4. $2\frac{1}{3}$ 5. $3\frac{1}{6}$ 6. $2\frac{5}{8}$ 7. $1\frac{4}{6}$

8. $3\frac{2}{5}$ 9. $1\frac{3}{4}$ 10. $4\frac{1}{3}$ 11. $2\frac{1}{2}$ 12. $2\frac{6}{8}$ 13. $3\frac{3}{4}$ 14. $1\frac{2}{6}$

❷ 8. $1\frac{3}{5}$ 9. $2\frac{1}{4}$ 10. $1\frac{2}{3}$ 11. $2\frac{1}{2}$ 12. $1\frac{2}{8}$ 13. $2\frac{1}{4}$ 14. $3\frac{4}{6}$

Fractions

1. $1\frac{1}{4}$ hours   2. $1\frac{3}{4}$ hours   3. $\frac{3}{4}$ hour   4. 2 hours   5. $1\frac{1}{2}$ hours

6. $2\frac{1}{4}$ hours   7. $3\frac{1}{4}$ hours   8. $1\frac{1}{3}$ km   9. $2\frac{1}{3}$ km   10. $1\frac{2}{3}$ km

11. $3\frac{1}{3}$ km   12. 1 km   13. 3 km   14. 4 km   15. $3\frac{2}{3}$ km

16. $5\frac{2}{3}$ km

Matching fractions

1. $\frac{1}{2} = \frac{2}{4}$ 2. $\frac{3}{4} = \frac{6}{8}, \frac{1}{4} = \frac{2}{8}$ 3. $\frac{2}{6} = \frac{1}{3}, \frac{4}{6} = \frac{2}{3}$ 4. $\frac{2}{3} = \frac{4}{6}, \frac{1}{3} = \frac{2}{6}$

5. $\frac{1}{3} = \frac{3}{9}, \frac{2}{3} = \frac{6}{9}$ 6. $\frac{2}{4} = \frac{4}{8}$ 7. $\frac{2}{8} = \frac{1}{4}, \frac{6}{8} = \frac{3}{4}$

8. $\frac{2}{4} = \frac{1}{2}$ 9. $\frac{2}{8} = \frac{1}{4}$ 10. $\frac{2}{2} = 1$ whole   11. $\frac{4}{8} = \frac{2}{4}$

12. $\frac{4}{8} = \frac{1}{2}$ 13. $\frac{4}{4} = 1$ whole   14. $\frac{6}{8} = \frac{3}{4}$ 15. $\frac{8}{8} = 1$ whole

---

Matching fractions

1. $\frac{1}{4} = \frac{2}{8}$ 2. $\frac{3}{4} = \frac{6}{8}$ 3. $\frac{1}{3} = \frac{2}{6}$ 4. $\frac{2}{3} = \frac{4}{6}$ 5. $\frac{1}{5} = \frac{2}{10}$ 6. $\frac{4}{5} = \frac{8}{10}$

❷ Answers will vary.

7. $\frac{2}{6} = \frac{1}{3}$ 8. $\frac{4}{6} = \frac{2}{3}$ 9. $\frac{3}{6} = \frac{1}{2}$ 10. $\frac{3}{3} = 1$ whole   11. $\frac{6}{6} = 1$ whole

Number Textbook 1

Matching fractions

1. $\frac{4}{10}$ **2.** $\frac{5}{10}$ **3.** $\frac{3}{10}$ **4.** $\frac{6}{10}$ **5.** $\frac{2}{10}$

6. $\frac{2}{6}$ **7.** $\frac{3}{6}$ **8.** $\frac{1}{6}$ **9.** $\frac{4}{6}$

@ $\frac{4}{10} = \frac{2}{5}$ $\frac{5}{10} = \frac{1}{2}$ $\frac{6}{10} = \frac{3}{5}$ $\frac{2}{10} = \frac{1}{5}$ $\frac{2}{6} = \frac{1}{3}$ $\frac{3}{6} = \frac{1}{2}$ $\frac{4}{6} = \frac{2}{3}$

Explore

$\frac{1}{2} = \frac{3}{6}$ $\frac{1}{2} = \frac{4}{8}$ $\frac{1}{2} = \frac{5}{10}$ $\frac{1}{3} = \frac{2}{6}$ $\frac{1}{4} = \frac{2}{8}$ $\frac{1}{5} = \frac{2}{10}$

$\frac{2}{3} = \frac{4}{6}$ $\frac{2}{3} = \frac{6}{9}$ $\frac{2}{5} = \frac{4}{10}$ $\frac{3}{4} = \frac{6}{8}$ $\frac{3}{5} = \frac{6}{10}$ $\frac{4}{5} = \frac{8}{10}$

12 pairs

Adding near multiples of 10

1. $4 + 30 = 34$ **2.** $17 + 19 = 36$ **3.** $23 + 29 = 52$ **4.** $38 + 29 = 67$
5. $45 + 29 = 74$ **6.** $52 + 39 = 91$ **7.** $66 + 19 = 85$ **8.** $79 + 21 = 100$
9. $81 + 11 = 92$ **10.** $94 + 39 = 133$

+	36	25	42	30	18	6	54	21
19	55	44	61	49	37	25	73	40
21	57	46	63	51	39	27	75	42
39	75	64	81	69	57	45	93	60

@ $36 + 59 = 95$ $25 + 59 = 84$ $42 + 59 = 101$ $30 + 59 = 89$
    $18 + 59 = 77$ $6 + 59 = 65$ $54 + 59 = 113$ $21 + 59 = 80$

Adding and subtracting near multiples of 10

1. $14 + 32 = 46$ **2.** $27 + 32 = 59$ **3.** $38 + 32 = 70$ **4.** $46 + 32 = 78$
5. $54 + 32 = 86$ **6.** $67 + 32 = 99$ **7.** $75 + 32 = 107$ **8.** $81 + 32 = 113$
9. $93 + 32 = 125$ **10.** $98 + 32 = 130$

11. $45 - 29 = 16$ **12.** $48 - 29 = 19$ **13.** $51 - 29 = 22$ **14.** $57 - 29 = 28$
15. $64 - 29 = 35$ **16.** $69 - 29 = 40$ **17.** $73 - 29 = 44$ **18.** $86 - 29 = 57$
19. $92 - 29 = 63$ **19a.** $95 - 29 = 66$

20. $275 - 29 = 246$ **21.** $432 - 29 = 403$ **22.** $556 + 39 = 595$
23. $674 - 39 = 635$ **24.** $783 - 49 = 734$ **25.** $326 + 49 = 375$
26. $245 - 39 = 206$

Number Textbook 1

Adding near multiples of 10

I. 45p + 39p = 84p   **2.** 53p + 39p = 92p   **3.** 28p + 39p = 67p
4. 38p + 39p = 77p   **5.** 35p + 39p = 74p   **6.** 47p + 39p = 86p
7. 58p + 39p = 97p   **8.** 69p + 39p = 108p = £1·08

@ I. 45p – 11p = 34p   **2.** 53p – 11p = 42p   **3.** 28p – 11p = 17p
4. 38p – 11p = 27p   **5.** 35p – 11p = 24p   **6.** 47p – 11p = 36p
7. 58p – 11p = 47p   **8.** 69p – 11p = 58p

Explore
Many different possible answers e.g. 39 + 49 + 59 + 89 = 236 (tens and/or hundreds digits must add to 200)

Subtracting near multiples of 10

I. 132 – 29 = 103   **2.** 246 – 29 = 217   **3.** 381 – 29 = 352
4. 163 – 29 = 134   **5.** 154 – 29 = 125   **6.** 443 – 29 = 414
7. 262 – 29 = 233   **8.** 191 – 29 = 162   **9.** 285 – 29 = 256

10. 67p – 39p = 28p   28p + 50p = 78p   has 78p now
II. 82 + 19 + 29 = 130 minutes   watched TV for 130 minutes
12. £42 – £19 = £23   £23 + £32 = £55   has £55 now

Adding multiples of 10

I. 24 + 13 = 37   240 + 130 = 370   **2.** 16 + 12 = 28   160 + 120 = 280
3. 17 + 5 = 22   170 + 50 = 220   **4.** 25 + 8 = 33   250 + 80 = 330
5. 23 + 24 = 47   230 + 240 = 470   **6.** 13 + 9 = 22   130 + 90 = 220
7. 34 + 6 = 40   340 + 60 = 400   **8.** 15 + 7 = 22   150 + 70 = 220
9. 42 + 21 = 63   420 + 210 = 630   **10.** 63 + 14 = 77   630 + 140 = 770

@ Answers will vary.

II. 230 + 140 = 370 cm   **12.** 310 + 140 = 450 cm
13. 210 + 140 = 350 cm   **14.** 420 + 140 = 560 cm
15. 360 + 140 = 500 cm   **16.** 750 + 140 = 890 cm
17. 860 + 140 = 1000 cm

Number Textbook 1

Adding multiples of 10

1.	$4 + 7 = 11$	$40 + 70 = 110$	$400 + 700 = 1100$
2.	$8 + 6 = 14$	$80 + 60 = 140$	$800 + 600 = 1400$
3.	$3 + 12 = 15$	$30 + 120 = 150$	$300 + 1200 = 1500$
4.	$16 + 7 = 23$	$160 + 70 = 230$	$1600 + 700 = 2300$
5.	$9 + 15 = 24$	$90 + 150 = 240$	$900 + 1500 = 2400$
6.	$13 + 9 = 22$	$130 + 90 = 220$	$1300 + 900 = 2200$
7.	$14 + 11 = 25$	$140 + 110 = 250$	$1400 + 1100 = 2500$
8.	$22 + 14 = 36$	$220 + 140 = 360$	$2200 + 1400 = 3600$
9.	$7 + 17 = 24$	$70 + 170 = 240$	$700 + 1700 = 2400$
10.	$9 + 19 = 28$	$90 + 190 = 280$	$900 + 1900 = 2800$

11. £140 + £50 = £190   12. £230 + £50 = £280
13. £310 + £50 = £360   14. £440 + £50 = £490

@ 11. £310   12. £220   13. £140   14. £10

Subtracting multiples of 10

1.	$13 - 7 = 6$	$130 - 70 = 60$	2.	$18 - 9 = 9$	$180 - 90 = 90$
3.	$24 - 8 = 16$	$240 - 80 = 160$	4.	$21 - 6 = 15$	$210 - 60 = 150$
5.	$34 - 7 = 27$	$340 - 70 = 270$	6.	$23 - 12 = 11$	$230 - 120 = 110$
7.	$36 - 8 = 28$	$360 - 80 = 280$	8.	$42 - 9 = 33$	$420 - 90 = 330$
9.	$27 - 13 = 14$	$270 - 130 = 140$	10.	$63 - 9 = 54$	$630 - 90 = 540$

11. $540 - 110 = 430$ 12. $170 - 80 = 90$ 13. $210 - 110 = 100$

14. $1200 - 700 = 500$ cm   15. $1500 - 700 = 800$ cm
16. $2100 - 700 = 1400$ cm   17. $2400 - 700 = 1700$ cm

@ 14. $500 - 400 = 100$ cm   15. $800 - 400 = 400$ cm
16. $1400 - 400 = 1000$ cm   17. $1700 - 400 = 1300$ cm

Subtracting multiples of 10

1.	$23 - 12 = 11$	$230 - 120 = 110$	$2300 - 1200 = 1100$
2.	$32 - 6 = 26$	$320 - 60 = 260$	$3200 - 600 = 2600$
3.	$28 - 7 = 21$	$280 - 70 = 210$	$2800 - 700 = 2100$
4.	$21 - 9 = 12$	$210 - 90 = 120$	$2100 - 900 = 1200$
5.	$17 - 11 = 6$	$170 - 110 = 60$	$1700 - 1100 = 600$
6.	$16 - 8 = 8$	$160 - 80 = 80$	$1600 - 800 = 800$
7.	$34 - 12 = 22$	$340 - 120 = 220$	$3400 - 1200 = 2200$

Number Textbook 1

8. $45 - 9 = 36$ $450 - 90 = 360$ $4500 - 900 = 3600$
9. $53 - 11 = 42$ $530 - 110 = 420$ $5300 - 1100 = 4200$
10. $49 - 13 = 36$ $490 - 130 = 360$ $4900 - 1300 = 3600$

@ $600 + 800 + 2200 + 3600 + 4200 + 3600 = 15000$

11. $80 + 30 + 20 = 130$ page 130
12. £270 + £80 = £350 £350 − £150 = £200 £200 left

---

page 55 Place-value **N16**
4-digit numbers

1. 2317, 2318, 2319 **2.** 4240, 4241, 4242 **3.** 3108, 3109, 3110
4. 5446, 5456, 5466 **5.** 4730, 4740, 4750 **6.** 3200, 3210, 3220
7. 4416, 4516, 4616 **8.** 8004, 8104, 8204 **9.** 2179, 2279, 2379
10. 4825, 5825, 6825 **11.** 5167, 6167, 7167 **12.** 4006, 5006, 6006

@ **1.** 2315, 2314, 2313 **2.** 4238, 4237, 4236
  3. 3106, 3105, 3104 **4.** 5426, 5416, 5406
  5. 4710, 4700, 4690 **6.** 3180, 3170, 3160
  7. 4216, 4116, 4016 **8.** 7804, 7704, 7604
  9. 1979, 1879, 1779 **10.** 2825, 1825, 825
  11. 3167, 2167, 1167 **12.** 2006, 1006, 6

13. 2349 **14.** 3426 **15.** 2474 **16.** 2650 **17.** 3090
18. 4099 **19.** 2799 **20.** 3116

---

page 56 Place-value **N16**
4-digit numbers

1. 33 **2.** 113 **3.** 344 **4.** 578, 589 **5.** 251
6. 392 **7.** 317 **8.** 536, 646 **9.** 660, 770 **10.** 430, 440

11. 1974 **12.** 1502 **13.** 581 **14.** 1076 **15.** 1818
16. 1600 **17.** 1676 **18.** 1339 **19.** 2009

@ 581, 1076, 1339, 1502, 1600, 1676, 1818, 1974, 2009

---

page 57 Place-value **N16**
3-digit and 4-digit numbers

1. 2256 km **2.** 4782 km **3.** 3445 km **4.** 7234 km **5.** 5904 km
6. 6149 km **7.** 2973 km **8.** 9420 km **9.** 9330 km **10.** 5051 km
11. 4410 km **12.** 1143 km

Number Textbook 1

page 57 cont ...

 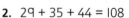

Distances in order
1143 km, 2256 km, 2973 km, 3445 km, 4410 km, 4782 km, 5051 km,
5904 km, 6149 km, 7234 km, 9330 km, 9420 km

Explore
Answers will vary.

---

page 58
Adding several 2-digit numbers

Addition/subtraction N17

1. $26 + 37 + 25 = 88$
2. $19 + 63 + 25 = 107$
3. $24 + 86 + 25 = 135$
4. $33 + 72 + 25 = 130$
5. $38 + 74 + 25 = 137$
6. $43 + 55 + 25 = 123$
7. $46 + 68 + 25 = 139$

8. $35 + 43 + 25 = 103$
9. $62 + 17 + 25 = 104$
10. $42 + 25 + 37 = 104$
11. $51 + 19 + 26 = 96$
12. $38 + 42 + 16 = 96$
13. $24 + 32 + 28 = 84$
14. $35 + 28 + 17 = 80$
15. $43 + 22 + 18 = 83$

---

page 59
Adding several 2-digit numbers

Addition/subtraction N17

1. $32p + 29p + 22p = 83p$
2. $27p + 34p + 17p = 78p$
3. $38p + 36p + 25p = 99p$
4. $36p + 22p + 17p = 75p$
5. $34p + 22p + 36p = 92p$
6. $29p + 27p + 38p = 94p$
7. $32p + 17p + 38p = 87p$

@ Answers will vary.

8. $35 + 45 + 17 = 97$
9. $96 + 4 + 18 = 118$
10. $42 + 37 + 19 = 98$
11. $52 + 25 + 18 = 95$
12. $43 + 34 + 25 = 102$
13. $27 + 28 + 29 = 84$
14. $48 + 45 + 35 = 128$
15. $28 + 38 + 48 = 114$

---

page 60
Adding several 2-digit numbers

Addition/subtraction N17

1. $27 + 36 + 42 = 105$
2. $29 + 35 + 44 = 108$
3. $27 + 35 + 44 = 106$ or $42 + 29 + 35 = 106$
4. $27 + 29 + 35 = 91$
5. $27 + 36 + 44 = 107$ or $36 + 42 + 29 = 107$
6. $27 + 29 + 44 = 100$ or $36 + 29 + 35 = 100$
7. $42 + 35 + 44 = 121$
8. $27 + 36 + 29 = 92$
9. $42 + 29 + 44 = 115$ or $36 + 35 + 44 = 115$
10. $27 + 36 + 35 = 98$ or $27 + 42 + 29 = 98$

Number Textbook 1

◉ 104, 113, 122, 109

27 + 42 + 35 = 104
27 + 42 + 44 = 113 or 36 + 42 + 35 = 113
36 + 42 + 44 = 122
36 + 29 + 44 = 109

11. 72 + 32 + 47 = 151   page 151
12. £48 + £22 + £27 = £97   she has £97

---

page 61
Addition/subtraction N17
Adding several 2-digit numbers

1. 27 + 15 + 13 = 55 km
2. 24 + 8 + 26 = 58 km
3. 23 + 26 + 15 = 64 km
4. 24 + 9 + 23 = 56 km
5. 24 + 13 + 12 = 49 km
6. 22 + 13 + 15 = 50 km
7. 12 + 24 + 22 = 58 km
8. 13 + 22 + 9 = 44 km

Explore
Various answers possible, e.g. a = 2, b = 4, c = 1, d = 7, e = 6 (24 + 21 + 17 = 62)

---

page 62
Addition/subtraction N18
Adding multiples of 10

1. 342 + 40 = 382
2. 725 + 30 = 755
3. 551 + 40 = 591
4. 329 + 50 = 379
5. 218 + 70 = 288
6. 424 + 70 = 494
7. 643 + 40 = 683
8. 183 + 10 = 193
9. 325 + 70 = 395
10. 469 + 30 = 499

11. £445 + £50 = £495
12. £225 + £50 = £275
13. £342 + £50 = £392
14. £236 + £50 = £286
15. £320 + £50 = £370
16. £516 + £50 = £566

---

page 63
Addition/subtraction N18
Adding multiples of 10

1. 216 + 80 = 296 m
2. 325 + 70 = 395 m
3. 248 + 50 = 298 m
4. 139 + 70 = 209 m
5. 314 + 90 = 404 m
6. 527 + 40 = 567 m
7. 243 + 80 = 323 m
8. 128 + 90 = 218 m
9. 417 + 50 = 467 m

◉ **1.** 496 m **2.** 595 m **3.** 498 m **4.** 409 m **5.** 604 m **6.** 767 m
7. 523 m **8.** 418 m **9.** 667 m

Number Textbook 1

Explore
16 additions

415 + 90 = 505	465 + 40 = 505
410 + 95 = 505	460 + 45 = 505
425 + 80 = 505	475 + 30 = 505
420 + 85 = 505	470 + 35 = 505
435 + 70 = 505	485 + 20 = 505
430 + 75 = 505	480 + 25 = 505
445 + 60 = 505	495 + 10 = 505
440 + 65 = 505	490 + 15 = 505

---

page 64   Addition/subtraction   N18
Adding multiples of 10 and 100

1. £117 + £160 = £277
2. £239 + £160 = £399
3. £406 + £160 = £566
4. £319 + £160 = £479
5. £224 + £160 = £384
6. £133 + £160 = £293
7. £253 + £160 = £413
8. £111 + £160 = £271
9. £142 + £160 = £302

10. 358 + 20 + 30 = 408   408 runs
11. 421 + 40 + 20 = 481   481 runs
12. 451 + 30 + 10 = 491   491 runs

---

page 65   Addition/subtraction   N19
Subtracting 2-digit numbers

1. 43 − 27 = 16
2. 42 − 18 = 24
3. 72 − 38 = 34
4. 61 − 25 = 36
5. 54 − 17 = 37
6. 64 − 27 = 37
7. 44 − 26 = 18
8. 56 − 38 = 18
9. 62 − 25 = 37
10. 73 − 28 = 45
11. 51 − 25 = 26
12. 82 − 38 = 44
13. 84 − 36 = 48
14. 75 − 17 = 58
15. 43 − 25 = 18
16. 53 − 24 = 29
17. 64 − 28 = 36
18. 74 − 38 = 36

---

page 66   Addition/subtraction   N19
Subtracting 2-digit numbers

1. 82 − 53 = 29
2. 82 − 66 = 16
3. 82 − 35 = 47
4. 82 − 58 = 24
5. 82 − 48 = 34
6. 82 − 37 = 45
7. 82 − 45 = 37
8. 82 − 27 = 55
9. 82 − 64 = 18
10. 82 − 55 = 27
11. 82 − 25 = 57
12. 82 − 63 = 19

Number Textbook 1

Explore

80, 55	71, 46	96, 71	62, 37	87, 62	53, 28	78, 53
44, 19	69, 44	35, 10	60, 35	51, 26	42, 17	

(other 3- and 4-digit numbers possible)

---

page 67   Addition/subtraction   N19

Subtracting 2-digit numbers

1. $92 - 78 = 14$ minutes   2. $84 - 58 = 26$ minutes
3. $92 - 38 = 54$ minutes   4. $104 - 86 = 18$ minutes
5. $94 - 62 = 32$ minutes   6. $112 - 92 = 20$ minutes
7. $86 - 67 = 19$ minutes   8. $125 - 91 = 34$ minutes
9. $110 - 64 = 46$ minutes   10. $98 - 66 = 32$ minutes

@ 1. $92 + 78 = 170$ minutes   2. $84 + 58 = 142$ minutes
3. $92 + 38 = 130$ minutes   4. $104 + 86 = 190$ minutes
5. $94 + 62 = 156$ minutes   6. $112 + 92 = 204$ minutes
7. $86 + 67 = 153$ minutes   8. $125 + 91 = 216$ minutes
9. $110 + 64 = 174$ minutes   10. $98 + 66 = 164$ minutes

11. $83 - 47 = 36$ 12. $61 - 28 = 33$ 13. $52 - 18 = 34$ 14. $72 - 37 = 35$
15. $92 - 45 = 47$ 16. $64 - 26 = 38$ 17. $55 - 18 = 37$ 18. $73 - 25 = 48$
19. $87 - 36 = 51$ 20. $94 - 27 = 67$

---

page 68   Addition/subtraction   N20

Subtracting 2-digit numbers

1. $63 - 35 = 28$ 2. $72 - 25 = 47$ 3. $81 - 43 = 38$ 4. $93 - 38 = 55$
5. $65 - 28 = 37$ 6. $73 - 37 = 36$ 7. $82 - 45 = 37$ 8. $54 - 28 = 26$
9. $64 - 17 = 47$ 10. $51 - 23 = 28$

11. $63 - 8 = 55$ 12. $72 - 7 = 65$ 13. $54 - 8 = 46$ 14. $41 - 7 = 34$
15. $33 - 8 = 25$ 16. $62 - 7 = 55$ 17. $91 - 8 = 83$ 18. $42 - 5 = 37$
19. $34 - 8 = 26$ 20. $63 - 7 = 56$

21. $72 - 29 = 43$ 22. $54 - 19 = 35$ 23. $61 - 39 = 22$ 24. $75 - 49 = 26$
25. $37 - 19 = 18$ 26. $64 - 49 = 15$ 27. $71 - 29 = 42$ 28. $66 - 29 = 37$
29. $55 - 39 = 16$ 30. $46 - 19 = 27$

Number Textbook 1

Subtracting 2-digit numbers

1. $53 - 35 = 18$ seconds
2. $62 - 25 = 37$ seconds
3. $81 - 36 = 45$ seconds
4. $74 - 39 = 35$ seconds
5. $64 - 37 = 27$ seconds
6. $44 - 19 = 25$ seconds
7. $34 - 29 = 5$ seconds

❷ 1. $53 + 35 = 88$ seconds
2. $62 + 25 = 87$ seconds
3. $81 + 36 = 117$ seconds
4. $74 + 39 = 113$ seconds
5. $64 + 37 = 101$ seconds
6. $44 + 19 = 63$ seconds
7. $34 + 29 = 63$ seconds

8. $72 - 45 = 27$
9. $68 - 45 = 23$
10. $92 - 45 = 47$
11. $73 - 45 = 28$
12. $62 - 45 = 17$
13. $58 - 45 = 13$

Subtracting 2-digit numbers

1. $91 - 68 = 23$ cm
2. $45 - 29 = 16$ cm
3. $93 - 64 = 29$ cm
4. $42 - 18 = 24$ cm
5. $51 - 29 = 22$ cm
6. $33 - 8 = 25$ cm
7. $88 - 75 = 13$ cm

8. $62 - 37 = 25$ 25 km to go
9. $42 - 15 = 27$ missed 27 minutes
10. $125 - 82 = 43$ needs 43 g more

Subtracting 2-digit numbers

1. $74 - 58 = 16$ km
2. $91 - 59 = 32$ km
3. $82 - 6 = 76$ km
4. $74 - 35 = 39$ km
5. $66 - 29 = 37$ km
6. $72 - 8 = 64$ km
7. $38 - 16 = 22$ km
8. $90 - 49 = 41$ km
9. $75 - 39 = 36$ km
10. $46 - 9 = 37$ km

❷ 1. $74 + 58 = 132$ km
2. $91 + 59 = 150$ km
3. $82 + 6 = 88$ km
4. $74 + 35 = 109$ km
5. $66 + 29 = 95$ km
6. $72 + 8 = 80$ km
7. $38 + 16 = 54$ km
8. $90 + 49 = 139$ km
9. $75 + 39 = 114$ km
10. $46 + 9 = 55$ km

Number Textbook 1

Explore

Possible amounts:

[Gareth, Dave] 46p, 1p	47p, 2p	48p, 3p	49p, 4p	50p, 5p
51p, 6p	52p, 7p	53p, 8p	54p, 9p	55p, 10p	56p, 11p
57p, 12p	58p, 13p	59p, 14p	60p, 15p	61p, 16p	62p, 17p
63p, 18p	64p, 19p	65p, 20p	66p, 21p	67p, 22p	68p, 23p
69p, 24p	70p, 25p	71p, 26p	72p, 27p		

---

page 72
Mixed problems

1. Clockwise cycle returns to original number. All the operations combined
   are the same as performing one operation of multiplying by 10. Crossing off
   the last digit of a number multiplied by 10 (0) will always leave the original
   digit.
2. £6 + £19 = £25
   £25 − £5 = £20
   £20 + £10 = £30
   £30 − £8 = £22
   £22 ÷ 2 = £11
   They have £11 each.
3. Mystery number is 34.

Number Textbook 2

Counting in 2s

1. 22, 24, 26, 28, 30, 32
2. 34, 36, 38, 40, 42, 44
3. 46, 48, 50, 52, 54, 56
4. 12, 14, 16, 18, 20, 22
5. 52, 50, 48, 46, 44, 42
6. 10, 8, 6, 4, 2, 0
7. 40, 42, 44, 46, 48, 50
8. 76, 78, 80, 82, 84, 86
9. 84, 82, 80, 78, 76, 74

| 12 | 24 | 32 | 36 | 38 | 40 | 50 | 58 | 68 | 74 |

Counting in 5s and 10s

1. 75	2. 100	3. 40	4. 25	5. 65	6. 60
7. 15	8. 20	9. 30	10. 35	11. 70	12. 80
13. 85	14. 10	15. 15	16. 100	17. 45	

ⓔ 1. 80   2. 100   3. 40   4. 30   5. 70   6. 60   7. 20   8. 20   9. 30
    10. 40   11. 70   12. 80   13. 90   14. 10   15. 20   16. 100   17. 50

31	32	33	34	(35)	36	37	38	39	(40)
41	42	43	44	(45)	46	47	48	49	(50)
51	52	53	54	(55)	56	57	58	59	(60)
61	62	63	64	(65)	66	67	68	69	(70)

Counting in 3s and 4s

1. £3·50   2. £3·50   3. £3·00   4. £2·50   5. £3·00   6. £3·00   7. £2·50

ⓔ   Any multiple of 12.

Explore
60

Number Textbook 2

Sizes

1. $4 \times 6 = 24$
2. $6 \times 6 = 36$
3. $8 \times 6 = 48$
4. $3 \times 6 = 18$
5. $5 \times 6 = 30$
6. $1 \times 6 = 6$
7. $9 \times 6 = 54$
8. $7 \times 6 = 42$
9. $10 \times 6 = 60$
10. $2 \times 6 = 12$

11. $4 \times 6 = 24$
12. $3 \times 6 = 18$
13. $5 \times 6 = 30$
14. $2 \times 6 = 12$
15. $7 \times 6 = 42$
16. $10 \times 6 = 60$
17. $8 \times 6 = 48$
18. $6 \times 6 = 36$
19. $1 \times 6 = 6$
20. $9 \times 6 = 54$

@   6   12   18   24   30   36   42   48   54   60   66   72

Sizes

1. $36 \div 6 = 6$
2. $12 \div 6 = 2$
3. $60 \div 6 = 10$
4. $24 \div 6 = 4$
5. $30 \div 6 = 5$
6. $18 \div 6 = 3$
7. $42 \div 6 = 7$
8. $48 \div 6 = 8$
9. $66 \div 6 = 11$
10. $54 \div 6 = 9$

@   1. 12   2. 4   3. 20   4. 8   5. 10   6. 6   7. 14   8. 16   9. 22   10. 18

11. $3 \times 6 = 18$
12. $7 \times 6 = 42$
13. $60 \div 6 = 10$
14. $5 \times 6 = 30$
15. $18 \div 6 = 3$
16. $6 \div 6 = 1$
17. $36 \div 6 = 6$
18. $9 \times 6 = 54$
19. $30 \div 6 = 5$
20. $54 \div 6 = 9$
21. $6 \times 6 = 36$
22. $24 \div 6 = 4$
23. $7 \times 6 = 42$

Sizes

1. $2 \times 3p = 6p$ $3 \times 6p = 18p$ $6p + 18p = 24p$
2. $3 \times 3p = 9p$ $4 \times 6p = 24p$ $9p + 24p = 33p$
3. $5 \times 3p = 15p$ $6 \times 6p = 36p$ $15p + 36p = 51p$
4. $1 \times 3p = 3p$ $4 \times 6p = 24p$ $3p + 24p = 27p$
5. $2 \times 3p = 6p$ $8 \times 6p = 48p$ $6p + 48p = 54p$
6. $9 \times 6p = 54p$
7. $4 \times 3p = 12p$ $5 \times 6p = 30p$ $12p + 30p = 42p$
8. $6 \times 3p = 18p$ $4 \times 6p = 24p$ $18p + 24p = 42p$

@   30p, 33p, 36p, 39p, 42p, 45p, 48p, 51p, 54p, 57p, 60p

Explore
Answers are all multiples of 3.

Number Textbook 2

Nines

I. $1 \times 9 = 9$	**2.** $2 \times 9 = 18$	**3.** $3 \times 9 = 27$	**4.** $4 \times 9 = 36$
5. $5 \times 9 = 45$	**6.** $6 \times 9 = 54$	**7.** $7 \times 9 = 63$	**8.** $8 \times 9 = 72$
9. $9 \times 9 = 81$	**10.** $10 \times 9 = 90$		

II. $4 \times 9 = 36$	**12.** $6 \times 9 = 54$	**13.** $5 \times 9 = 45$	**14.** $1 \times 9 = 9$
15. $3 \times 9 = 27$	**16.** $8 \times 9 = 72$	**17.** $9 \times 9 = 81$	**18.** $7 \times 9 = 63$
19. $2 \times 9 = 18$			

Nines

I. $45 \div 9 = 5$	**2.** $27 \div 9 = 3$	**3.** $9 \div 9 = 1$	**4.** $90 \div 9 = 10$
5. $63 \div 9 = 7$	**6.** $18 \div 9 = 2$	**7.** $54 \div 9 = 6$	**8.** $36 \div 9 = 4$
9. $72 \div 9 = 8$	**10.** $81 \div 9 = 9$		

II. $2 \times 9 = 18$	**12.** $5 \times 9 = 45$	**13.** $4 \times 9 = 36$	**14.** $9 \times 9 = 81$
15. $7 \times 9 = 63$	**16.** $8 \times 9 = 72$	**17.** $10 \times 9 = 90$	**18.** $3 \times 9 = 27$
19. $6 \times 9 = 54$			

Explore

| 18 | 27 | 36 | 45 | 90 | or | 81 | 72 | 63 | 54 | 90 |

Nines

	x 9 table		adding the digits	
I.	$2 \times 9 =$	18	$1 + 8 =$	9
2.	$3 \times 9 =$	27	$2 + 7 =$	9
3.	$4 \times 9 =$	36	$3 + 6 =$	9
4.	$5 \times 9 =$	45	$4 + 5 =$	9
5.	$6 \times 9 =$	54	$5 + 4 =$	9
6.	$7 \times 9 =$	63	$6 + 3 =$	9
7.	$8 \times 9 =$	72	$7 + 2 =$	9
8.	$9 \times 9 =$	81	$8 + 1 =$	9
9.	$10 \times 9 =$	90	$9 + 0 =$	9

Number Textbook 2

◉ **I.** 7   **2.** 5   **3.** 3   **4.** 1   **5.** 1   **6.** 3   **7.** 5   **8.** 7   **9.** 9
The differences are all consecutive odd numbers.

10. $5 \times 9 = 45$ $6 \times 9 = 54$ **II.** $4 \times 9 = 36$ $7 \times 9 = 63$
12. $3 \times 9 = 27$ $8 \times 9 = 72$ **13.** $2 \times 9 = 18$ $9 \times 9 = 81$
14. $1 \times 9 = 9$ $10 \times 9 = 90$

Sevens

I. $4 \times 7 = 28$ days   **2.** $2 \times 7 = 14$ days   **3.** $1 \times 7 = 7$ days
4. $6 \times 7 = 42$ days   **5.** $8 \times 7 = 56$ days   **6.** $7 \times 7 = 49$ days
7. $9 \times 7 = 63$ days   **8.** $5 \times 7 = 35$ days   **9.** $11 \times 7 = 77$ days
10. $10 \times 7 = 70$ days   **II.** $3 \times 7 = 21$ days   **12.** $12 \times 7 = 84$ days
13. $13 \times 7 = 91$ days

14. $4 \times 7 = 28$ **15.** $5 \times 7 = 35$ **16.** $2 \times 7 = 14$ **17.** $10 \times 7 = 70$
18. $3 \times 7 = 21$ **19.** $6 \times 7 = 42$ **20.** $11 \times 7 = 77$ **21.** $8 \times 7 = 56$
22. $7 \times 7 = 49$ **23.** $9 \times 7 = 63$

Sevens

I. $14 \div 7 = 2$ weeks   **2.** $28 \div 7 = 4$ weeks   **3.** $42 \div 7 = 6$ weeks
4. $49 \div 7 = 7$ weeks   **5.** $63 \div 7 = 9$ weeks   **6.** $35 \div 7 = 5$ weeks
7. $21 \div 7 = 3$ weeks   **8.** $70 \div 7 = 10$ weeks   **9.** $56 \div 7 = 8$ weeks

◉ Answers will vary.

10. $42 \div 7 = 6$ **II.** $14 \div 7 = 2$ **12.** $28 \div 7 = 4$ **13.** $70 \div 7 = 10$
14. $21 \div 7 = 3$ **15.** $7 \div 7 = 1$ **16.** $35 \div 7 = 5$ **17.** $56 \div 7 = 8$
18. $49 \div 7 = 7$ **19.** $63 \div 7 = 9$

◉ **10.** $6 \times 7 = 42$ **II.** $2 \times 7 = 14$ **12.** $4 \times 7 = 28$ **13.** $10 \times 7 = 70$
14. $3 \times 7 = 21$ **15.** $1 \times 7 = 7$ **16.** $5 \times 7 = 35$ **17.** $8 \times 7 = 56$
18. $7 \times 7 = 49$ **19.** $9 \times 7 = 63$

Number Textbook 2

Sevens

I	2	3	4	5	6	7	8	9	10
2	4	6	8	10	12	14	16	18	20
3	6	9	12	15	18	21	24	27	30
4	8	12	16	20	24	28	32	36	40
5	10	15	20	25	30	35	40	45	50
6	12	18	24	30	36	42	48	54	60
7	14	21	28	35	42	49	56	63	70
8	16	24	32	40	48	56	64	72	80
9	18	27	36	45	54	63	72	81	90
10	20	30	40	50	60	70	80	90	100

Numbers that appear most on grid: 6, 8, 10, 12, 18, 20, 24, 30, 40 (4 times)
Numbers that appear once only: 1, 25, 49, 64, 81, 100

I. $2 \times 7 = 14$ **2.** $5 \times 7 = 35$ **3.** $21 \div 7 = 3$ **4.** $35 \div 7 = 5$
5. $42 \div 7 = 6$ **6.** $9 \times 7 = 63$ **7.** $7 \div 7 = 1$ **8.** $8 \times 7 = 56$
9. $4 \times 7 = 28$ **10.** $77 \div 7 = 11$

Explore
7	14	21	28	35	42	49	56	63	70
77	84	91	98	105	112	119	126	133	140

Summing the digits of each number to a single digit:
7	5	3	1	8	6	4	2	9	7
5	3	1	8	6	4	2	9	7	5

Pattern: 7, 5, 3, 1, 8, 6, 4, 2, 9, 7, 5, ...

Number Textbook 2

Tens and hundreds

1. $13 \times 10p = 130p = £1·30$
2. $19 \times 10p = 190p = £1·90$
3. $23 \times 10p = 230p = £2·30$
4. $10 \times 10p = 100p = £1·00$
5. $21 \times 10p = 210p = £2·10$
6. $30 \times 10p = 300p = £3·00$
7. $22 \times 10p = 220p = £2·20$
8. $16 \times 10p = 160p = £1·60$
9. $15 \times 10p = 150p = £1·50$

10. 35 bananas
11. 1 banana
12. 10 bananas
13. 48 bananas
14. 28 bananas
15. 56 bananas
16. 42 bananas

Tens and hundreds

1. £1·50
2. £2·00
3. £1·10
4. 60p
5. £4·80
6. £3·60
7. £5·30

❷ 1. £15
2. £20
3. £11
4. £6
5. £48
6. £36
7. £53

8. 1200 cm
9. 1400 cm
10. 3100 cm
11. 600 cm
12. 5000 cm
13. 3600 cm
14. 2800 cm
15. 1800 cm
16. 6300 cm

Tens and hundreds

1. $400 \div 100 = 4$ boxes
2. $300 \div 100 = 3$ boxes
3. $900 \div 100 = 9$ boxes
4. $6000 \div 100 = 60$ boxes
5. $2500 \div 100 = 25$ boxes
6. $800 \div 100 = 8$ boxes
7. $7200 \div 100 = 72$ boxes

8. $70 \times 10 = 700$
9. $3 \times 100 = 300$
10. $700 \div 10 = 70$
11. $1000 \div 100 = 10$
12. $9000 \div 10 = 900$
13. $24 \times 10 = 240$
14. $40 \times 100 = 4000$
15. $800 \div 100 = 8$
16. $4000 \div 10 = 400$

17a. $£7·80 = 780p$ $780 \div 10 = 78$ 78 coins
  b. $78 + 15 = 93$ coins $93 \times 10p = 930p = £9·30$ has £9·30 now
  c. $£9·30 - £3·99 = £5·31$ has £5·31 left

Number Textbook 2

Multiplying

1. $3 \times 30p = 90p$
2. $3 \times 20p = 60p$
3. $3 \times 50p = 150p$
4. $3 \times 40p = 120p$
5. $3 \times 80p = 240p$
6. $3 \times 60p = 180p$
7. $3 \times £1 = £3$

1a. $4 \times 30p = 120p$
2a. $4 \times 20p = 80p$
3a. $4 \times 50p = 200p$
4a. $4 \times 40p = 160p$
5a. $4 \times 80p = 320p$
6a. $4 \times 60p = 240p$
7a. $4 \times £1 = £4$

1b. $2 \times 30p = 60p$
2b. $2 \times 20p = 40p$
3b. $2 \times 50p = 100p$
4b. $2 \times 40p = 80p$
5b. $2 \times 80p = 160p$
6b. $2 \times 60p = 120p$
7b. $2 \times £1 = £2$

8. $2 \times 10p = 20p$
9. $2 \times 60p = 120p$
10. $3 \times 30p = 90p$
11. $4 \times 20p = 80p$
12. $3 \times 50p = 150p$
13. $3 \times 40p = 120p$
14. $4 \times 40p = 160p$
15. $4 \times 30p = 120p$
16. $4 \times 60p = 240p$

Multiplying

1. 4×22

	20	2
4	80	8

$80 + 8 = 88$ buns

2. 4×24

	20	4
4	80	16

$80 + 16 = 96$ buns

3. 4×32

	30	2
4	120	8

$120 + 8 = 128$ buns

4. 4×15

	10	5
4	40	20

$40 + 20 = 60$ buns

5. 4×26

	20	6
4	80	24

$80 + 24 = 104$ buns

6. 4×19

	10	9
4	40	36

$40 + 36 = 76$ buns

Number Textbook 2

7. 4 x 41

```
        40   1
   4  | 160 | 4 |    160 + 4 = 164 buns
```

8. 4 x 23

```
        20   3
   4  | 80  | 12 |   80 + 12 = 92 buns
```

9. 4 x 36

```
        30   6
   4  | 120 | 24 |   120 + 24 = 144 buns
```

10. 4 x 34

```
        30   4
   4  | 120 | 16 |   120 + 16 = 136 buns
```

11. 4 x 11

```
        10   1
   4  | 40  | 4 |    40 + 4 = 44 buns
```

12. 2 x 21 = 40 + 2 = 42

13. 3 x 24 = 60 + 12 = 72

14. 4 x 31 = 120 + 4 = 124

15. 5 x 26 = 100 + 30 = 130

16. 4 x 24 = 80 + 16 = 96

17. 6 x 23 = 120 + 18 = 138

18. 2 x 43 = 80 + 6 = 86

19. 3 x 22 = 60 + 6 = 66

20. 5 x 33 = 150 + 15 = 165

21. 7 x 24 = 140 + 28 = 168

22. 8 x 42 = 320 + 16 = 336

23. 5 x 51 = 250 + 5 = 255

24. 9 x 15 = 90 + 45 = 135

25. 6 x 36 = 180 + 36 = 216

26. 3 x 34 = 90 + 12 = 102

27. 4 x 35 = 120 + 20 = 140

28. 2 x 32 = 60 + 4 = 64

Multiplying

1. 2 x 42p = 84p

2. 8 x 24p = 192p = £1·92

3. 5 x 53p = 265p = £2·65

4. 4 x 31p = 124p = £1·24

5. 3 x 62p = 186p = £1·86

6. 9 x 13p = 117p = £1·17

7. 4 x 53p = 212p = £2·12

8. 5 x 24p = 120p = £1·20

9. 7 x 62p = 434p = £4·34

10. 4 x 42p = 168p = £1·68

11. 3 x 13p = 39p

12. 7 x 31p = 217p = £2·17

13. 9 x 24p = 216p = £2·16

Explore

2 x 60 = 120, 3 x 40 = 120, 4 x 30 = 120, 5 x 24 = 120, 6 x 20 = 120, 8 x 15 = 120
2 x 72 = 144, 3 x 48 = 144, 4 x 36 = 144, 6 x 24 = 144, 8 x 18 = 144, 9 x 16 = 144

Number Textbook 2

Fractions

1. $\frac{3}{4}$ 2. $\frac{5}{6}$ 3. $\frac{3}{8}$ 4. $\frac{3}{5}$ 5. $\frac{5}{9}$ 6. $\frac{7}{10}$

7. $\frac{1}{8}$ 8. $\frac{1}{6}$ 9. $\frac{1}{10}$ 10. $\frac{1}{8}$ 11. $\frac{1}{2}$ 12. $\frac{2}{5}$

13. $\frac{3}{4}$ 14. $\frac{9}{10}$ 15. $\frac{4}{6}$ 16. $\frac{7}{9}$ 17. $\frac{3}{4}$ 18. $\frac{5}{8}$

ℯ $\frac{1}{10}, \frac{1}{9}, \frac{1}{8}, \frac{1}{6}, \frac{1}{4}, \frac{3}{8}, \frac{2}{5}, \frac{1}{2}, \frac{5}{9}, \frac{3}{5} = \frac{6}{10}, \frac{5}{8}, \frac{4}{6}, \frac{7}{10}, \frac{3}{4}, \frac{7}{9}, \frac{4}{5}, \frac{5}{6}, \frac{9}{10}$

Fractions

1. $\frac{3}{8}$ 2. $\frac{1}{3}$ 3. $\frac{3}{5}$ 4. $\frac{3}{4}$ 5. $\frac{3}{6}$ 6. $\frac{2}{3}$

7. $\frac{3}{5}$ 8. $\frac{5}{6}$ 9. $\frac{4}{8}$ 10. $\frac{2}{4}$

1a. $\frac{3}{8} < \frac{1}{2}$ 2a. $\frac{1}{3} < \frac{1}{2}$ 3a. $\frac{3}{5} > \frac{1}{2}$ 4a. $\frac{3}{4} > \frac{1}{2}$ 5a. $\frac{3}{6} = \frac{1}{2}$ 6a. $\frac{2}{3} > \frac{1}{2}$

7a. $\frac{3}{5} > \frac{1}{2}$ 8a. $\frac{5}{6} > \frac{1}{2}$ 9a. $\frac{4}{8} = \frac{1}{2}$ 10a. $\frac{2}{4} = \frac{1}{2}$

Explore
Answers will vary.

Fractions

a $\frac{1}{3}$ b $\frac{2}{3}$ c $\frac{1}{6}$ d $\frac{3}{6} = \frac{1}{2}$ e $\frac{4}{6} = \frac{2}{3}$ f $\frac{1}{4}$

g $\frac{2}{4} = \frac{1}{2}$ h $\frac{3}{4}$ i $\frac{1}{8}$ j $\frac{3}{8}$ k $\frac{5}{8}$ l $\frac{7}{8}$

1. $\frac{1}{3} > \frac{1}{4}$ 2. $\frac{1}{8} < \frac{1}{6}$ 3. $\frac{3}{6} = \frac{2}{4}$ 4. $\frac{3}{4} < \frac{7}{8}$ 5. $\frac{2}{3} = \frac{4}{6}$ 6. $\frac{3}{8} < \frac{2}{4}$

7. $\frac{5}{8} < \frac{4}{6}$ 8. $\frac{2}{3} < \frac{3}{4}$

9. $\frac{1}{3} < \frac{2}{3}$ 10. $\frac{3}{4} > \frac{1}{4}$ 11. $\frac{1}{5} < \frac{1}{2}$ 12. $\frac{1}{2} < \frac{3}{4}$ 13. $\frac{2}{3} > \frac{1}{5}$ 14. $\frac{4}{8} = \frac{2}{4}$

15. $\frac{7}{10} > \frac{2}{5}$ 16. $\frac{3}{6} = \frac{1}{2}$ 17. $\frac{4}{5} > \frac{3}{4}$

ℯ   Answers will vary.

Number Textbook 2

Fractions

1. $\frac{1}{4}$ of 12p = 3p   2. $\frac{2}{4}$ of 12p = 6p   3. $\frac{3}{4}$ of 12p = 9p

4. $\frac{4}{4}$ of 12p =12p   5. $\frac{1}{3}$ of 15p = 5p   6. $\frac{2}{3}$ of 15p = 10p

7. $\frac{3}{3}$ of 15p = 15p   8. $\frac{1}{5}$ of 20p = 4p   9. $\frac{2}{5}$ of 20p = 8p

10. $\frac{3}{5}$ of 20p = 12p   11. $\frac{4}{5}$ of 20p = 16p   12. $\frac{5}{5}$ of 20p = 20p

❷   Answers will vary.

Explore
Answers will vary.

Fractions

1. $\frac{1}{4}$ of 8 = 2   2. $\frac{1}{3}$ of 6 = 2   3. $\frac{3}{8}$ of 8 = 3   4. $\frac{3}{4}$ of 8 = 6

5. $\frac{2}{5}$ of 10 = 4   6. $\frac{2}{3}$ of 9 = 6   7. $\frac{2}{3}$ of 6 = 4   8. $\frac{5}{6}$ of 12 = 10

9. $\frac{1}{4}$ of 12 = 3   10. $\frac{4}{5}$ of 10 = 8

❷ 1. $\frac{1}{2}$ 2. $\frac{1}{6}$ 3. $\frac{1}{4}$ 4. $\frac{5}{8}$ 5. $\frac{3}{5}$ 6. $\frac{1}{3}$ 7. $\frac{1}{3}$ 8. $\frac{1}{3}$ 9. $\frac{1}{2}$ 10. $\frac{7}{10}$

11. $\frac{1}{3}$ of 9 = 3   12. $\frac{1}{4}$ of 8 = 2   13. $\frac{2}{4}$ of 8 = 4   14. $\frac{3}{4}$ of 8 = 6

15. $\frac{1}{3}$ of 6 = 2   16. $\frac{2}{3}$ of 6 = 4   17. $\frac{3}{3}$ of 6 = 6   18. $\frac{1}{2}$ of 12 = 6

19. $\frac{2}{4}$ of 12 = 6

Fractions

1. $\frac{2}{3}$ of 12 = 8   2. $\frac{5}{6}$ of 18 = 15   3. $\frac{1}{6}$ of 12 = 2   4. $\frac{2}{4}$ of 12 = 6

5. $\frac{4}{5}$ of 10 = 8   6. $\frac{2}{3}$ of 9 = 6   7. $\frac{1}{3}$ of 15 = 5   8. $\frac{1}{4}$ of 16 = 4

❷ 1. $\frac{1}{3}$ of 12 = 4   2. $\frac{1}{6}$ of 18 = 3   3. $\frac{5}{6}$ of 12 = 10   4. $\frac{2}{4}$ of 12 = 6

5. $\frac{1}{5}$ of 10 = 2   6. $\frac{1}{3}$ of 9 = 3   7. $\frac{2}{3}$ of 15 = 10   8. $\frac{3}{4}$ of 16 = 12

9. $\frac{3}{5}$ of barrel = 24 apples $\frac{1}{5}$ = 8 apples   8 x 5 = 40   40 apples in total

10. $\frac{1}{2}$ of £24 = £12 $\frac{1}{4}$ of £24 = £6 $\frac{1}{6}$ of £24 = £4

     £12 + £6 + £4 = £22   £24 − £22 = £2   he has £2 left

Number Textbook 2

Rounding

1. 366 → g	**2.** 374 → d	**3.** 367 → b	**4.** 379 → e
5. 371 → h	**6.** 361 → a	**7.** 370 → c	**8.** 378 → j
9. 375 → i	**10.** 364 → f		

1a. 366 → 370	**2a.** 374 → 370	**3a.** 367 → 370	**4a.** 379 → 380
5a. 371 → 370	**6a.** 361 → 360	**7a.** 370 → 370	**8a.** 378 → 380
9a. 375 → 380	**10a.** 364 → 360		

a 330 cm → 300 cm
b 360 cm → 400 cm
c 390 cm → 400 cm
d 620 cm → 600 cm
e 650 cm → 700 cm
f 690 cm → 700 cm
g 810 cm → 800 cm
h 840 cm → 800 cm
i 870 cm → 900 cm

Rounding

1. 258 g	**2.** 316 g	**3.** 211 g	**4.** 273 g	**5.** 385 g	**6.** 284 g
7. 357 g	**8.** 249 g	**9.** 332 g			

1a. 258 g → 260 g	258 g → 300 g	**2a.** 316 g → 320 g	316 g → 300 g
3a. 211 g → 210 g	211 g → 200 g	**4a.** 273 g → 270 g	273 g → 300 g
5a. 385 g → 390 g	385 g → 400 g	**6a.** 284 g → 280 g	284 g → 300 g
7a. 357 g → 360 g	357 g → 400 g	**8a.** 249 g → 250 g	249 g → 200 g
9a. 332 g → 330 g	332 g → 300 g		

Explore

427 → 430	427 → 400	472 → 470	472 → 500
724 → 720	724 → 700	742 → 740	742 → 700
247 → 250	247 → 200	274 → 270	274 → 300

Five nearest hundreds.

Rounding

1. 346p	**2.** 248p	**3.** 125p	**4.** 461p	**5.** 314p	**6.** 640p
7. 307p	**8.** 218p	**9.** 511p	**10.** 606p		

Number Textbook 2

1a. 346p → 350p   346p → 300p → £3
2a. 248p → 250p   248p → 200p → £2
3a. 125p → 130p   125p → 100p → £1
4a. 461p → 460p   461p → 500p → £5
5a. 314p → 310p   314p → 300p → £3
6a. 640p → 640p   640p → 600p → £6
7a. 307p → 310p   307p → 300p → £3
8a. 218p → 220p   218p → 200p → £2
9a. 511p → 510p   511p → 500p → £5
10a. 606p → 610p   606p → 600p → £6

Explore
Numbers with 460 as the nearest ten: 455, 456, 457, 458, 459, 460, 461, 462, 463, 464
One hundred answers altogether. Answers will vary.

---

page 30
Addition/subtraction   N30
Adding two numbers

1. 226 + 180 = 406   **2.** 416 + 375 = 791   **3.** 175 + 236 = 411
4. 244 + 367 = 611   **5.** 364 + 138 = 502   **6.** 333 + 579 = 912
7. 565 + 236 = 801   **8.** 109 + 463 = 572   **9.** 277 + 524 = 801

10. 283 + 158 = 441 m   **11.** 294 + 158 = 452 m   **12.** 178 + 158 = 336 m
13. 227 + 158 = 385 m   **14.** 199 + 158 = 357 m   **15.** 285 + 158 = 443 m
16. 207 + 158 = 365 m

---

page 31
Addition/subtraction   N30
Adding 3-digit numbers

1. 255 g + 375 g = 630 g   **2.** 341 g + 489 g = 830 g
3. 248 g + 367 g = 615 g   **4.** 371 g + 299 g = 670 g
5. 176 g + 265 g = 441 g   **6.** 353 g + 448 g = 801 g
7. 527 g + 366 g = 893 g   **8.** 234 g + 259 g = 493 g
9. 619 g + 191 g = 810 g   **10.** 355 g + 455 g = 810 g

402 + 98 = 500   226 + 274 = 500   236 + 264 = 500   178 + 322 = 500
244 + 256 = 500   358 + 142 = 500

Number Textbook 2

Adding 3-digit numbers

1. $96 + 124 + 78 + 168 = 466$ runs
2. $87 + 225 + 184 + 96 = 592$ runs
3. $123 + 214 + 119 + 267 = 723$ runs
4. $75 + 242 + 98 + 108 = 523$ runs
5. $256 + 125 + 118 + 87 = 586$ runs
6. $144 + 241 + 109 + 218 = 712$ runs

Explore
Answers will vary.
Highest possible score is 3, by making 1000.

Subtracting multiples of 10

1. $367 - 80 = 287$
2. $256 - 80 = 176$
3. $373 - 80 = 293$
4. $552 - 80 = 472$
5. $147 - 80 = 67$
6. $608 - 80 = 528$
7. $431 - 80 = 351$
8. $824 - 80 = 744$
9. $912 - 80 = 832$

@ $287 - 50 = 237$ $176 - 50 = 126$ $293 - 50 = 243$ $472 - 50 = 422$
$67 - 50 = 17$ $528 - 50 = 478$ $351 - 50 = 301$ $744 - 50 = 694$
$832 - 50 = 782$

10. $374 - 80 = 294$
11. $254 - 70 = 184$
12. $171 - 90 = 81$
13. $554 - 60 = 494$
14. $333 - 60 = 273$
15. $742 - 80 = 662$
16. $681 - 90 = 591$
17. $625 - 70 = 555$
18. $423 - 50 = 373$
19. $217 - 40 = 177$
20. $892 - 70 = 822$
21. $711 - 60 = 651$

Subtracting multiples of 10

1. $116 - 30 = 86$ minutes
2. $121 - 40 = 81$ minutes
3. $119 - 50 = 69$ minutes
4. $127 - 60 = 67$ minutes
5. $142 - 90 = 52$ minutes
6. $123 - 70 = 53$ minutes
7. $122 - 30 = 92$ minutes
8. $132 - 50 = 82$ minutes
9. $118 - 60 = 58$ minutes

$243 - 60 = 183$ $332 - 60 = 272$ $418 - 60 = 358$
$243 - 70 = 173$ $332 - 70 = 262$ $418 - 70 = 348$
$243 - 80 = 163$ $332 - 80 = 252$ $418 - 80 = 338$

Number Textbook 2

Subtracting multiples of 10

–	241	321	106	445	211
30	211	291	76	415	181
60	181	261	46	385	151
80	161	241	26	365	131
20	221	301	86	425	191

1. £123 – £60 = £63   £63 left
2. 107 – 70 = 37   37 years old
   107 – 30 = 77   77 years old
3. 500 – 90 = 410   410 pieces
   410 – 80 = 330   330 pieces to do
4. 578 – 80 = 498   498 people left
   498 – 50 = 448   448 people left

Subtracting

1. 123 – 56 = 67   2. 173 – 88 = 85   3. 142 – 65 = 77
4. 214 – 178 = 36   5. 123 – 76 = 47   6. 122 – 67 = 55
7. 204 – 166 = 38   8. 214 – 155 = 59   9. 184 – 95 = 89
10. 133 – 74 = 59   11. 311 – 294 = 17   12. 177 – 67 = 110
13. 405 – 328 = 77   14. 338 – 282 = 56

15. 121 – 38 = 83 minutes   16. 126 – 38 = 88 minutes
17. 132 – 38 = 94 minutes   18. 144 – 38 = 106 minutes
19. 137 – 38 = 99 minutes   20. 118 – 38 = 80 minutes

Subtracting

1. 114 – 65 = 49   2. 186 – 71 = 115   3. 223 – 126 = 97
4. 119 – 47 = 72   5. 253 – 198 = 55   6. 207 – 114 = 93
7. 245 – 133 = 112   8. 118 – 53 = 65   9. 302 – 213 = 89

10. 243 – 167 = 76   11. 314 – 268 = 46   12. 417 – 347 = 70
13. 624 – 586 = 38   14. 709 – 644 = 65   15. 313 – 277 = 36
16. 424 – 386 = 38   17. 503 – 479 = 24   18. 257 – 134 = 123
19. 303 – 223 = 80

Number Textbook 2

page 38
Subtracting

1. 343 – 157 = 186 miles
3. 411 – 274 = 137 miles
5. 454 – 232 = 222 miles
7. 413 – 102 = 311 miles

2. 241 – 173 = 68 miles
4. 236 – 91 = 145 miles
6. 318 – 107 = 211 miles

e 1. 343 + 157 = 500 miles
3. 411 + 274 = 685 miles
5. 454 + 232 = 686 miles
7. 413 + 102 = 515 miles

2. 241 + 173 = 414 miles
4. 236 + 91 = 327 miles
6. 318 + 107 = 425 miles

Explore
Answers will vary.
Smallest possible difference: 723 – 684 = 39 or 426 – 387 = 39
Largest possible difference: 876 – 234 = 642
Nearest difference to 400: 862 – 473 = 398

---

page 39
Subtracting

1. 346 – 129 = 217
4. 463 – 245 = 218
7. 562 – 226 = 336
10. 273 – 129 = 144
13. 912 – 431 = 481
16. 332 – 170 = 162

2. 537 – 162 = 375
5. 471 – 322 = 149
8. 672 – 348 = 324
11. 614 – 372 = 242
14. 504 – 271 = 233
17. 406 – 282 = 124

3. 341 – 225 = 116
6. 564 – 127 = 437
9. 372 – 148 = 224
12. 727 – 366 = 361
15. 456 – 271 = 185

814 – 459 = 355
943 – 459 = 484
721 – 459 = 262

814 – 367 = 447
943 – 367 = 576
721 – 367 = 354

814 – 188 = 626
943 – 188 = 755
721 – 188 = 533

---

page 40
Subtracting

1. 336 – 183 = 153
4. 337 – 148 = 189
7. 329 – 155 = 174
10. 327 – 164 = 163

2. 528 – 262 = 266
5. 347 – 158 = 189
8. 337 – 165 = 172

3. 328 – 191 = 137
6. 364 – 192 = 172
9. 403 – 181 = 222

Number Textbook 2

Ia. 183 – 153 = 30   **2a.** 266 – 262 = 4   **3a.** 191 – 137 = 54
4a. 189 – 148 = 41   **5a.** 189 – 158 = 31   **6a.** 192 – 172 = 20
7a. 174 – 155 = 19   **8a.** 172 – 165 = 7   **9a.** 222 – 181 = 41
10a. 164 – 163 = 1

---

page 41   Addition/subtraction
Subtracting

I. 472 – 216 = 256 g   **2.** 224 – 157 = 67 g   **3.** 336 – 172 = 164 g
4. 417 – 208 = 209 g   **5.** 293 – 144 = 149 g   **6.** 515 – 273 = 242 g
7. 483 – 197 = 286 g   **8.** 377 – 159 = 218 g   **9.** 333 – 177 = 156 g

10. 237 – 128 = 109   109 boys
II. 365 – 176 = 189   189 days

---

page 42   Properties of number
Odd and even

I. 472   even   **2.** 555   odd   **3.** 641   odd
4. 229   odd   **5.** 318   even   **6.** 744   even
7. 908   even   **8.** 163   odd   **9.** 227   odd
10. 842   even   **II.** 669   odd   **12.** 343   odd
13. 516   even   **14.** 732   even

15. 78, 80, 82   **16.** 116, 118, 120   **17.** 310, 312, 314
18. 968, 970, 972   **19.** 196, 198, 200   **20.** 438, 440, 442
21. 514, 516, 518   **22.** 666, 668, 670   **23.** 798, 800, 802
24. 444, 446, 448   **25.** 396, 398, 400   **26.** 108, 110, 112
27. 998, 1000, 1002

ⓔ

15. 74, 76   **16.** 112, 114   **17.** 306, 308   **18.** 964, 966
19. 192, 194   **20.** 434, 436   **21.** 510, 512   **22.** 662, 664
23. 794, 796   **24.** 440, 442   **25.** 392, 394   **26.** 104, 106
27. 994, 996

Number Textbook 2

Odd and even

+	1	2	3	4	5	6
1	2	3	4	5	6	7
2	3	4	5	6	7	8
3	4	5	6	7	8	9
4	5	6	7	8	9	10
5	6	7	8	9	10	11
6	7	8	9	10	11	12

= blue

= yellow

= red

odd + odd = even
even + even = even
odd + even = even + odd = odd

1. 7 + 9 even
2. 5 + 6 odd
3. 23 + 37 even
4. 42 + 54 even
5. 16 + 12 even
6. 54 + 17 odd
7. 513 + 123 even
8. 138 + 223 odd
9. 565 + 363 even

Explore

Pairs with even totals: 7, 5   2, 4   7, 9   1, 5   3, 7   2, 8   1, 7   9, 5   (8 pairs)

Pairs with odd totals: 3, 8   8, 1   2, 7   4, 9   9, 6   3, 2   8, 7   5, 6   4, 7
8, 5   7, 6   2, 9   (12 pairs)

Number Textbook 2

–	7	8	9	10	11	12
1	6	7	8	9	10	11
2	5	6	7	8	9	10
3	4	5	6	7	8	9
4	3	4	5	6	7	8
5	2	3	4	5	6	7
6	1	2	3	4	5	6

= blue

= yellow

= red

odd – odd = even
even – even = even
odd – even = even – odd = odd

1. $15 - 9 = 6$ $8 - 7 = 1$
    $24 - 12 = 12$ Bob's winnings £1 + £1 + 50p = £2·50
2. $12 - 8 = 4$ $18 - 9 = 9$
    $13 - 7 = 6$ Sanjit's winnings £1 + £1 + 50p = £2·50
3. $9 - 3 = 6$ $11 - 6 = 5$
    $21 - 14 = 7$ Jenna's winnings £1 + 50p + 50p = £2
4. $11 - 2 = 9$ $24 - 6 = 18$
    $17 - 9 = 8$ Tim's winnings £1 + £1 + 50p = £2·50
5. $18 - 12 = 6$ $22 - 18 = 4$
    $16 - 9 = 7$ Jo's winnings £1 + £1 + 50p = £2·50

---

  1. ⁻4 °C   **2.** ⁻2°C   **3.** ⁻3 °C   **4.** ⁻7 °C   **5.** ⁻1 °C
  6. ⁻6 °C   **7.** ⁻8 °C

❷ 1. ⁻2 °C **2.** 0 °C **3.** ⁻1 °C **4.** ⁻5 °C **5.** 1 °C **6.** ⁻4 °C **7.** ⁻6 °C

  8. ⁻6 °C   **9.** ⁻9 °C   **10.** ⁻4 °C   **11.** ⁻2 °C   **12.** ⁻7 °C
13. ⁻10 °C   **14.** ⁻12 °C   **15.** ⁻3 °C

Number Textbook 2

Properties of number **N35**

Negative numbers

a. $18 - 8 = 10$ **b.** $14 - 8 = 6$ **c.** $8 - 8 = 0$
d. $4 - 8 = {}^-4$ **e.** $1 - 8 = {}^-7$ **f.** ${}^-2 - 8 = {}^-10$
g. ${}^-5 - 8 = {}^-13$ **h.** ${}^-9 - 8 = {}^-17$ **i.** ${}^-12 - 8 = {}^-20$
j. ${}^-16 - 8 = {}^-24$

ⓔ a. 14   **b.** 10   **c.** 4   **d.** 0   **e.** ${}^-3$ **f.** ${}^-6$ **g.** ${}^-9$ **h.** ${}^-13$ **i.** ${}^-16$ **j.** ${}^-20$

1. ${}^-18\ °C \rightarrow {}^-14\ °C$ **2.** ${}^-14\ °C \rightarrow {}^-17\ °C$ **3.** ${}^-17\ °C \rightarrow {}^-12\ °C$
4. ${}^-12\ °C \rightarrow {}^-10\ °C$ **5.** ${}^-10\ °C \rightarrow {}^-18\ °C$ **6.** ${}^-18\ °C \rightarrow {}^-12\ °C$
7. ${}^-12\ °C \rightarrow {}^-5\ °C$ **8.** ${}^-5\ °C \rightarrow {}^-18\ °C$

Properties of number **N35**

Negative numbers

1. Sam still owes 5p.   **2.** Lily still owes 3p.   **3.** Chuy still owes 10p.
4. Bill still owes 5p.   **5.** Simone still owes 6p.   **6.** Jon still owes 9p.
7. Hatti still owes 4p.   **8.** Samira still owes 6p.   **9.** Dan still owes 18p.
10. Amrita still owes 5p.   **11.** Jack still owes 11p.   **12.** Mel still owes 11p.
13. Vikram still owes 18p.

Explore

$5 + {}^-6 = {}^-1$ $4 + {}^-5 = {}^-1$ $3 + {}^-4 = {}^-1$ $2 + {}^-3 = {}^-1$ $1 + {}^-2 = {}^-1$ 5 pairs

---

Multiplication/division **N36**

Doubling

1. double $360 = 600 + 120 = 720$ g   **2.** double $240 = 400 + 80 = 480$ g
3. double $310 = 600 + 20 = 620$ g   **4.** double $170 = 200 + 140 = 340$ g
5. double $380 = 600 + 160 = 760$ g   **6.** double $460 = 800 + 120 = 920$ g
7. double $190 = 200 + 180 = 380$ g

8. double $240 = 400 + 80 = 480$ **9.** double $330 = 600 + 60 = 660$
10. double $260 = 400 + 120 = 520$ **11.** double $470 = 800 + 140 = 940$
12. double $180 = 200 + 160 = 360$ **13.** double $250 = 400 + 100 = 500$
14. double $390 = 600 + 180 = 780$

Number Textbook 2

Halving

1. half of 780 m = 350 + 40 = 390 m   2. half of 540 m = 250 + 20 = 270 m
3. half of 460 m = 200 + 30 = 230 m   4. half of 830 m = 400 + 15 = 415 m
5. half of 920 m = 450 + 10 = 460 m   6. half of 340 m = 150 + 20 = 170 m
7. half of 590 m = 250 + 45 = 295 m

8. half of £580 = 250 + 40 = £290   9. half of £760 = 350 + 30 = £380
10. half of £440 = 200 + 20 = £220   11. half of £320 = 150 + 10 = £160
12. half of £650 = 300 + 25 = £325   13. half of £940 = 450 + 20 = £470
14. half of £380 = 150 + 40 = £190

Doubling and halving

1. 6800 potatoes   9200 carrots   3600 onions   5400 tomatoes
    4200 celery sticks   880 pints of stock
2. 1700 potatoes   2300 carrots   900 onions   1350 tomatoes
    1050 celery sticks   220 pints of stock
3. 850 potatoes   1150 carrots   450 onions   675 tomatoes
    525 celery sticks   110 pints of stock

double

in	out
2300	4600
4500	9000
1700	3400
480	960
3700	7400
290	580
3100	6200

halve

in	out
6800	3400
780	390
4900	2450
2700	1350
8600	4300
930	465
5800	2900

Multiplying

1. 22 x 4 = 88   2. 12 x 3 = 36   3. 32 x 2 = 64   4. 15 x 3 = 45
5. 14 x 5 = 70   6. 35 x 2 = 70   7. 38 x 4 = 152   8. 56 x 2 = 112
9. 29 x 3 = 87   10. 45 x 7 = 315

Number Textbook 2

Multiplication/division

11. 27 x 5 = 135   **12.** 15 x 4 = 60   **13.** 21 x 5 = 105   **14.** 32 x 5 = 160
15. 51 x 4 = 204   **16.** 28 x 5 = 140   **17.** 43 x 6 = 258   **18.** 37 x 4 = 148
19. 35 x 7 = 245   **20.** 62 x 5 = 310

---

page 52
Multiplication/division   N37
Multiplying

1. 31p x 5 = 155p = £1·55   **2.** 26p x 4 = 104p = £1·04
3. 18p x 5 = 90p   **4.** 42p x 6 = 252p = £2·52
5. 26p x 7 = 182p = £1·82   **6.** 31p x 8 = 248p = £2·48
7. 14p x 7 = 98p

8. 32p x 6 = 192p = £1·92   **9.** 13p x 5 = 65p
10. 43p x 4= 172p = £1·72   **11.** 21p x 6 = 126p = £1·26
12. 13p x 8 = 104p = £1·04   **13.** 32p x 7 = 224p = £2·24
14. 28p x 4 = 112p = £1·12

---

page 53
Multiplication/division   N37
Multiplying

1. 23 x 4 = 92 m   **2.** 17 x 6 = 102 m   **3.** 14 x 5 = 70 m
4. 22 x 4 = 88 m   **5.** 13 x 8 = 104 m   **6.** 34 x 4 = 136 m
7. 21 x 6 = 126 m   **8.** 49 x 4 = 196 m

@   Answers will vary.

Explore
Largest possible answer: 43 x 5 = 215   Smallest possible answer: 34 x 2 = 68
24 different answers

---

page 54
Multiplication/division
Dividing

1. 32p ÷ 10 = 3p r 2p   **2.** 44p ÷ 10 = 4p r 4p
3. 69p ÷ 10 = 6p r 9p   **4.** 71p ÷ 10 = 7p r 1p
5. 83p ÷ 10 = 8p r 3p   **6.** 104p ÷ 10 = 10p r 4p
7. 67p ÷ 10 = 6p r 7p   **8.** 70p ÷ 10 = 7p
9. 58p ÷ 10 = 5p r 8p

@   Answers will vary.

Number Textbook 2

10. $46 \div 5 = 9$ r 1
11. $13 \div 3 = 4$ r 1
12. $11 \div 2 = 5$ r 1
13. $37 \div 5 = 7$ r 2
14. $21 \div 2 = 10$ r 1
15. $16 \div 5 = 3$ r 1
16. $23 \div 3 = 7$ r 2
17. $28 \div 5 = 5$ r 3
18. $25 \div 2 = 12$ r 1

page 55   Multiplication/division **N38**
Dividing

1. $22 \div 5 = 4$ r 2   r = 2 bones
2. $43 \div 5 = 8$ r 3   r = 3 bones
3. $31 \div 5 = 6$ r 1   r = 1 bone
4. $29 \div 5 = 5$ r 4   r = 4 bones
5. $17 \div 5 = 3$ r 2   r = 2 bones
6. $58 \div 5 = 11$ r 3   r = 3 bones
7. $42 \div 5 = 8$ r 2   r = 2 bones
8. $64 \div 5 = 12$ r 4   r = 4 bones
9. $75 \div 5 = 15$ r = 0 bones

10. $42 \div 5 = 8$ r 2
11. $20 \div 6 = 3$ r 2
12. $38 \div 9 = 4$ r 2
13. $33 \div 8 = 4$ r 1
14. $28 \div 3 = 9$ r 1
15. $49 \div 6 = 8$ r 1
16. $15 \div 4 = 3$ r 3
17. $43 \div 8 = 5$ r 3
18. $66 \div 9 = 7$ r 3

page 56   Multiplication/division **N38**
Dividing

1. $42 \div 5 = 8$ r 2   needed 9 tubes
2. $47 \div 5 = 9$ r 2   can buy 9 tickets
3. $6 \times 7 = 42$ $42 + 3 = 45$ 45 cakes
4. $47 \div 7 = 6$ r 5   5 players not in a team

5. $28 \div 3 = 9$ r 1
6. $28 \div 2 = 14$
7. $28 \div 8 = 3$ r 4
8. $28 \div 9 = 3$ r 1
9. $28 \div 5 = 5$ r 3
10. $28 \div 6 = 4$ r 4
12. $28 \div 7 = 4$

Explore
Numbers that divide into 20 exactly: 1, 2, 4, 5, 10, 20
Numbers that divide into 12 exactly: 1, 2, 3, 4, 6, 12
Numbers that divide into 30 exactly: 1, 2, 3, 5, 6, 10, 15, 30
Numbers that divide into 24 exactly: 1, 2, 3, 4, 6, 8, 12, 24

page 57   Multiplication/division **N39**
Dividing

1. $4\overline{)48} = 12$ groups
2. $2\overline{)24} = 12$ groups
3. $2\overline{)36} = 18$ groups
4. $3\overline{)39} = 13$ groups
5. $4\overline{)64} = 16$ groups
6. $3\overline{)69} = 23$ groups
7. $5\overline{)85} = 17$ groups
8. $3\overline{)57} = 19$ groups
9. $4\overline{)76} = 19$ groups

Number Textbook 2

10. $2\overline{)32} = 16$ **11.** $3\overline{)69} = 23$ **12.** $5\overline{)85} = 17$ **13.** $4\overline{)68} = 17$
14. $2\overline{)48} = 24$ **15.** $6\overline{)78} = 13$ **16.** $6\overline{)96} = 16$ **17.** $7\overline{)91} = 13$
18. $5\overline{)65} = 13$ **19.** $3\overline{)96} = 32$ **20.** $7\overline{)98} = 14$ **21.** $4\overline{)76} = 19$

---

page 58
Dividing

1. $4\overline{)52} = 13$ torches   **2.** $3\overline{)63} = 21$ torches   **3.** $6\overline{)78} = 13$ torches
4. $4\overline{)84} = 21$ torches   **5.** $3\overline{)72} = 24$ torches   **6.** $3\overline{)66} = 22$ torches
7. $4\overline{)84} = 21$ torches   **8.** $6\overline{)84} = 14$ torches   **9.** $3\overline{)93} = 31$ torches
10. $2\overline{)64} = 32$ torches   **11.** $3\overline{)72} = 24$ torches

12. $2\overline{)88} = 44$ **13.** $3\overline{)48} = 16$ **14.** $4\overline{)72} = 18$ **15.** $5\overline{)75} = 15$
16. $2\overline{)74} = 37$ **17.** $3\overline{)87} = 29$ **18.** $4\overline{)64} = 16$ **19.** $3\overline{)75} = 25$
20. $2\overline{)92} = 46$ **21.** $3\overline{)81} = 27$ **22.** $3\overline{)93} = 31$

---

page 59
Dividing

1. $84 \div 4 = 21$ 21 packs
2. $£96 \div 3 = £32$ £32 each
3. $65 \div 5 = 13$ bought 13 crayons
4. $96 \div 6 = 16$ 16 cm long

5. $6\overline{)73} = 12$ r 1   **6.** $4\overline{)66} = 16$ r 2   **7.** $7\overline{)81} = 11$ r 4
8. $3\overline{)47} = 15$ r 2   **9.** $4\overline{)58} = 14$ r 2

Explore
61

---

page 60
Tenths

1. $\frac{3}{10}$ **2.** $\frac{5}{10}$ **3.** $\frac{4}{10}$ **4.** $\frac{2}{10}$ **5.** $\frac{1}{10}$

6. $\frac{8}{10}$ **7.** $\frac{10}{10}$ **8.** $\frac{6}{10}$ **9.** $\frac{9}{10}$ **10.** $\frac{7}{10}$

1a. $\frac{3}{10} = 0.3$ **2a.** $\frac{5}{10} = 0.5$ **3a.** $\frac{4}{10} = 0.4$ **4a.** $\frac{2}{10} = 0.2$ **5a.** $\frac{1}{10} = 0.1$

6a. $\frac{8}{10} = 0.8$ **7a.** $\frac{10}{10} = 1.0$ **8a.** $\frac{6}{10} = 0.6$ **9a.** $\frac{9}{10} = 0.9$ **10a.** $\frac{7}{10} = 0.7$

Number Textbook 2

a 0·4 m	**b** 0·9 m	**c** 1·2 m	**b** 1·7 m	**e** 2·1 m
f 2·6 m	**g** 3·0 m	**h** 3·6 m	**i** 4·3 m	**j** 4·8 m
k 5·1 m	**l** 5·9 m			

---

page 61

Tenths

1. h	**2.** c	**3.** f	**4.** e	**5.** a
6. i	**7.** b	**8.** d	**9.** g	

10. 2·4 kg	**11.** 3·6 kg	**12.** 2·5 kg	**13.** 1·3 kg	**14.** 3·8 kg
15. 4·2 kg	**16.** 0·6 kg			

---

page 62

Tenths

1·1 kg, 1·3 kg, 1·7 kg, 2·6 kg, 2·9 kg, 3·6 kg, 3·9 kg, 4·0 kg, 4·2 kg, 4·7 kg, 5·1 kg, 5·3 kg

Explore

6 numbers

2·3	2·5	3·2	3·5	5·2	5·3

---

page 63

Hundredths

1. £1·25	**2.** £2·52	**3.** £1·31	**4.** £3·30	**5.** £5·10
6. £0·53	**7.** £0·37	**8.** £0·77	**9.** £1·04	**10.** £6·07

11. a = 2·12 b = 2·14 c = 2·17 d = 2·19

12. a = 3·23 b = 3·26 c = 3·29 d = 3·35 e = 3·39

13. a = 8·62 b = 8·65 c = 8·66 d = 8·71 e = 8·74 f = 8·78

---

page 64

Hundredths

1. 2·25 m	**2.** 1·32 m	**3.** 1·20 m	**4.** 1·30 m
5. 0·5 m or 0·50 m	**6.** 0·45 m	**7.** 2·56 m	**8.** 3·60 m
9. 4·5 m or 4·50 m	**10.** 1·25 m		

Number Textbook 2

page 64 cont ...
Fractions/decimals

11. k   **12.** d   **13.** i   **14.** f   **15.** b   **16.** g
17. c   **18.** a   **19.** j   **20.** h   **21.** e

---

page 65
Fractions/decimals

Hundredths

1. £3·17   **2.** £5·15   **3.** £1·18   **4.** £3·40   **5.** £5·00
6. £3·05   **7.** £7·00   **8.** £7·81   **9.** £1·91   **10.** £7·01
11. £8·03   **12.** £4·41   **13.** £1·83

14. £8·80   **15.** £7·01   **16.** £4·97   **17.** £5·09   **18.** £9·79
19. £2·99   **20.** £3·89   **21.** £4·48

---

page 66
Addition/subtraction

Subtracting

1. $445 - 257 = 188$ **2.** $356 - 288 = 68$ **3.** $264 - 159 = 105$
4. $437 - 258 = 179$ **5.** $548 - 289 = 259$ **6.** $185 - 97 = 88$
7. $244 - 166 = 78$ **8.** $343 - 157 = 186$ **9.** $322 - 165 = 157$
10. $345 - 177 = 168$

11. $564 - 287 = 277$ **12.** $473 - 296 = 177$ **13.** $885 - 297 = 588$
14. $664 - 488 = 176$ **15.** $837 - 478 = 359$

---

page 67
Addition/subtraction

Subtracting

1. $911 - 281 = 630$ km   **2.** $911 - 324 = 587$ km   **3.** $911 - 365 = 546$ km
4. $911 - 482 = 429$ km   **5.** $911 - 543 = 368$ km   **6.** $911 - 664 = 247$ km
7. $911 - 727 = 184$ km   **8.** $911 - 786 = 125$ km   **9.** $911 - 875 = 36$ km

$716 - 345 = 371$ $716 - 488 = 228$ $716 - 698 = 18$
$924 - 345 = 579$ $924 - 488 = 436$ $924 - 698 = 226$
$833 - 345 = 488$ $833 - 488 = 345$ $833 - 698 = 135$

---

page 68
Addition/subtraction

Subtracting

1. $242 - 115 = 127$ m   **2.** $621 - 136 = 485$ m   **3.** $221 - 85 = 136$ m
4. $624 - 460 = 164$ m

Number Textbook 2

5. $213 - 124 = 89$ m   6. $321 - 236 = 85$ m   7. $263 - 172 = 91$ m
8. $305 - 218 = 87$ m

9. $518 - 348 = 170$ m   10. $646 - 527 = 119$ m   11. $685 - 658 = 27$ m
12. $902 - 893 = 9$ m

Explore
Answers will vary.

---

page 69   Addition/subtraction **N43**
Adding and subtracting

1. £5·68 + £4·87 = £10·55
2. £13·58 + £7·77 = £21·35
3. £15·49 + £12·75 = £28·24
4. £9·99 + £11·11 = £21·10
5. £4·75 + £3·86 = £8·61
6. £10·49 + £12·87 = £23·36
7. £9·87 + £13·56 = £23·43
8. £9·19 + £7·77 = £16·96
9. £11·29 + £14·98 = £26·27
10. £8·76 + £12·41 = £21·17

11. £4·11 − £2·22 = £1·89
12. £3·50 − £1·75 = £1·75
13. £6·12 − £4·24 = £1·88
14. £4·20 − £1·80 = £2·40
15. £3·17 − £1·77 = £1·40
16. £2·80 − £1·90 = £0·90

---

page 70   Addition/subtraction **N43**
Subtracting

1. £3·29 − £1·79 = £1·50   2. £5·59 − £3·89 = £1·70
3. £6·38 − £2·98 = £3·40   4. £4·37 − £1·67 = £2·70
5. £10·16 − £2·96 = £7·20   6. £5·29 − £2·79 = £2·50
7. £8·16 − £1·46 = £6·70   8. £7·57 − £3·87 = £3·70
9. £4·26 − £2·76 = £1·50   10. £6·28 − £3·98 = £2·30

£9·98, £7·99   £6·67, £4·68   £3·73, £1·74   £7·54, £5·55   £5·35, £3·36

Number Textbook 2

Subtracting

1. £19·99 − £8·78 = £11·21
3. £19·99 − £11·12 = £8·87
5. £19.99 − £13·75 = £6·24
7. £19·99 − £11·79 = £8·20

2. £19·99 − £10·19 = £9·80
4. £19·99 − £5·50 = £14·49
6. £19·99 − £13·64 = £6·35
8. £19·99 − £15·75 = £4·24

Explore
Jane is 12, James is 6.

page 72
Mixed problems

1. 346 m + 168 m = 514 m   1000 m − 514 m = 486 m   486 m further
2. 346 g + 425 g + 475 g + 582 g = 1828 g   2 x 1828 g = 3656 g
   total weight now 3656 g
3a. 512 − 468 = 44   Mark scored 44 more
 b. Jinda   468 + 275 = 743
    Mark   512 + 196 = 708
    Jinda wins by 35
 c. Jinda   743 − 500 = 243   final score   243 points
    Mark   708 − 400 = 308   final score   308 points
4a. £12·99 + £13·79 + £11·69 = £38·47   £38·50 − £38·47 = 3p
 b. Cannot buy 4 videos for £45, cheapest option £45·26.

Shape, Data and Measures

Centimetres (cm)

1. 4 cm	**2.** 6 cm	**3.** 8 cm	**4.** 3 cm	**5.** 10 cm
6. 7 cm	**7.** 5 cm			

❷   40 mm   60 mm   80 mm   30 mm   100 mm   70 mm   50 mm

8–13. Estimates and answers will vary.

Centimetres (cm), metres (m), millimetres (mm)

1. 120 cm	**2.** 105 cm	**3.** 2 cm	**4.** 180 cm
5. 230 cm	**6.** 4 cm	**7.** 156 cm	

8. 1 m 30 cm	**9.** 2 m 20 cm	**10.** 3 m 50 cm
11. 2 m	**12.** 5 cm 4 mm	**13.** 6 cm 8 mm
14. 9 cm 7 mm	**15.** 6 cm	

Metres (m) and kilometres (km)

1. 2 km 543 m	**2.** 3 km 342 m	**3.** 2 km 230 m
4. 4 km 100 m	**5.** 6 km 12 m	**6.** 1 km 111 m
7. 3 km 921 m	**8.** 3 km 403 m	**9.** 1 km 45 m

❷

1. 1 km 271·5 m	**2.** 1 km 671 m	**3.** 1 km 115 m	**4.** 2 km 50 m
5. 3 km 6 m	**6.** 555·5 m	**7.** 1 km 960·5 m	**8.** 1 km 701·5 m
9. 522·5 m			

10. $300 \div 5 = 60$	$60 \times 3 = 180$ miles
11. $100 \div 5 = 20$	$20 \times 3 = 60$ miles
12. $1000 \div 5 = 200$	$200 \times 3 = 600$ miles
13. $650 \div 5 = 130$	$130 \times 3 = 390$ miles
14. $250 \div 5 = 50$	$50 \times 3 = 150$ miles
15. $350 \div 5 = 70$	$70 \times 3 = 210$ miles
16. $10 \div 5 = 2$	$2 \times 3 = 6$ miles
17. $500 \div 5 = 100$	$100 \times 3 = 300$ miles
18. $50 \div 5 = 10$	$10 \times 3 = 30$ miles
19. $90 \div 5 = 18$	$18 \times 3 = 54$ miles
20. $85 \div 5 = 17$	$17 \times 3 = 51$ miles

Shape, Data and Measures

page 6

Grams (g) and kilograms (kg)

1. 1700 g	**2.** 1200 g	**3.** 2300 g
4. 3150 g	**5.** 1900 g	**6.** 4100 g
7. 2500 g		

8. 1 kg 500 g	**9.** 2 kg 300 g	**10.** 1 kg 700 g
11. 3 kg	**12.** 4 kg 500 g	**13.** 1 kg 50 g
14. 2 kg 505 g	**15.** 1 kg 675 g	**16.** 1 kg 225 g

page 7

Grams (g) and kilograms (kg)

1–7. Answers will vary.

8. 2	**9.** 4	**10.** 20	**11.** 40	**12.** 8
13. 10	**14.** 4	**15.** 5	**16.** 80	

Explore
Put the 1 kg weight on one side of the balance and each kitten in turn on the other side until it balances. This kitten weighs 1 kg. Next put the three remaining kittens on opposite sides of the balance to find the one that always makes the balance go down. This kitten is the heaviest – 1 kg 300 g. Then put the two remaining kittens on opposite sides of the balance. The heavier one is 1 kg 200 g; the lighter one is 1 kg 100 g.

page 8

Grams (g) and kilograms (kg)

1–8. Estimates will vary.

1. grams	**2.** grams	**3.** grams	**4.** kilograms
5. kilograms	**6.** kilograms	**7.** kilograms	**8.** grams

9. $4 \times 200 \text{ g} = 800\text{g}$ $1000 \text{ g} - 800 \text{ g} = 200\text{g}$ 200 g left

10. $25 \text{ kg} - 2\frac{1}{2} \text{ kg} = 22\frac{1}{2} \text{ kg}$ $22\frac{1}{2} \text{ kg} + \frac{3}{4} \text{ kg} = 23\frac{1}{4} \text{ kg}$

Shape, Data and Measures

page 9

Millilitres (ml) and litres (l)

I. 1200 ml   **2.** 1400 ml   **3.** 400 ml   **4.** 200 ml
5. 700 ml   **6.** 300 ml   **7.** 1000 ml   **8.** 900 ml
9. 1800 ml

10. 1 l 700 ml   **II.** 2 l 300 ml   **12.** 2 l 500 ml
13. 2 l 650 ml   **14.** 1 l 850 ml   **15.** 1 l 900 ml
16. 4 l   **17.** 1 l 500 ml   **18.** 2 l 350 ml

page 10

Litres and pints

I. 8 pints   **2.** 6 pints   **3.** 4 pints
4. 13 pints   **5.** 14 pints   **6.** 24 pints
7. 17 pints   **8.** 11 pints   **9.** 30 pints

10. 1 litre   **II.** 3·5 litres   **12.** 2 litres
13. 1·5 litres   **14.** 4·5 litres

10. $9 - 2 = 7$ 7 pints $\approx 3\frac{1}{2}$ litres   **II.** $9 - 7 = 2$ 2 pints $\approx$ 1 litre
12. $9 - 4 = 5$ 5 pints $\approx 2\frac{1}{2}$ litres   **13.** $9 - 3 = 6$ 6 pints $\approx$ 3 litres
14. $9 - 9 = 0$ 0 pints $\approx$ 0 litres

page 11

Litres (l) and millilitres (ml)

I. 20 x 75p = 1500p = £15   **2.** 40 x 75p = 3000p = £30
3. 30 x 75p = 2250p = £22·50   **4.** 50 x 75p = 3750p = £37·50
5. 10 x 75p = 750p = £7·50   **6.** 100 x 75p = 7500p = £75
7. 110 x 75p = 8250p = £82·50

8. 1 + 3 + 3 + 3 + 2 = 12 doses   12 x 5 ml = 60 ml
9. 1000 ml – 200 ml = 800 ml   800 ml ÷ 4 = 200 ml each

page 12

Area

I. A = 15 cm²   **2.** A = 30 cm²   **3.** A = 20 cm²   **4.** A = 6 cm²
5. A = 3 cm²   **6.** A = 12 cm²   **7.** A = 12 cm²

Shape, Data and Measures

page 12 cont ...

8. A = 14 cm²   **9.** A = 9 cm²   **10.** A = 8 cm²   **11.** A = 12 cm²
12. A = 12 cm²   **13.** A = 16 cm²

---

page 13

Area

1. A = 11 cm²   **2.** A = 18 cm²   **3.** A = 8 cm²   **4.** A = 7 cm²
5. A = 16 cm²   **6.** A = 26 cm²   **7.** A = 5 cm²   **8.** A = 10 cm²
9. A = 13 cm²

Explore
Answers will vary.

---

page 14

Area

1. A = 9 cm²   **2.** A = 25 cm²   **3.** A = 10 cm²   **4.** A = 4 cm²
5. A = 13 cm²   **6.** A = 31 cm²   **7.** A = 24 cm²   **8.** A = 22 cm²

9. 8 cm x 5 cm = 40 cm²   7 cm x 6 cm = 42 cm²   42 cm² – 40 cm² = 2 cm²
difference in area is 2 cm²
10. 3 m x 8 m = 24 m²   24 m² x 4 = 96 m²   96 m² ÷ 32 m² = 3
Chris needs 3 tins

---

page 15

Perimeter and area

1. P = 8 cm   **2.** P = 8 cm   **3.** P = 12 cm   **4.** P = 14 cm
5. P = 10 cm   **6.** P = 16 cm   **7.** P = 12 cm   **8.** P = 12 cm
9. P = 16 cm   **10.** P = 14 cm

3 shapes with same perimeter are **3**, **7** and **8**.

1. A = 3 cm²   **2.** A = 4 cm²   **3.** A = 5 cm²   **4.** A = 6 cm²
5. A = 6 cm²   **6.** A = 12 cm²   **7.** A = 9 cm²   **8.** A = 8 cm²
9. A = 7 cm²   **10.** A = 10 cm²

Shape, Data and Measures

page 15 cont ...

Explore

square	perimeter (cm)	area (cm²)
1 x 1	4	1
2 x 2	8	4
3 x 3	12	9
4 x 4	16	16
etc.		

The perimeter is the length of the sides multiplied by 4.
The area is the length of the sides multiplied by itself.
The 10th square will have perimeter 40 cm and area 100 cm².

page 16

Perimeter and area

1. P = 8 cm   A = 3 cm²
2. P = 12 cm   A = 5 cm²
3. P = 12 cm   A = 5 cm²
4. P = 12 cm   A = 5 cm²
5. P = 16 cm   A = 7 cm²
6. P = 12 cm   A = 5 cm²
7. P = 12 cm   A = 5 cm²
8. P = 12 cm   A = 5 cm²
9. P = 12 cm   A = 5 cm²

@ 45 cm²

Explore
Answers will vary.

page 17

Perimeter

1. 15 m x 2 = 30 m   5 m x 2 = 10 m   perimeter = 40 m
2. 16 m x 2 = 32 m   10 m x 2 = 20 m   perimeter = 52 m
3. 14 m x 2 = 28 m   5 m x 2 = 10 m   perimeter = 38 m
4. 18 m x 2 = 36 m   5 m x 2 = 10 m   perimeter = 46 m
5. 13 m x 2 = 26 m   10 m x 2 = 20 m   perimeter = 46 m
6. 16 m x 2 = 32 m   8 m x 2 = 16 m   perimeter = 48 m

Shape, Data and Measures

page 17 cont ...

● **1.** 75 m²   **2.** 160 m²   **3.** 70 m²   **4.** 90 m²

   5. 130 m²   **6.** 128 m²

7. 20 cm x 2 = 40 cm   30 cm x 2 = 60 cm   40 cm x 2 = 80 cm
   50 cm x 2 = 100 cm   40 cm + 60 cm + 80 cm + 100 cm = 280 cm ribbon

8. Various possible answers e.g. 20 cm x 30 cm – dimensions must add to 50 cm

---

page 18
Minutes

Time **M6**

1. 13 minutes   **2.** 22 minutes   **3.** 52 minutes   **4.** 38 minutes

5. 33 minutes   **6.** 40 minutes   **7.** 42 minutes   **8.** 29 minutes

9. 57 minutes   **10.** 4 minutes   **11.** 18 minutes   **12.** 6 minutes

13. 14 minutes

1a. 47 minutes   **2a.** 38 minutes   **3a.** 8 minutes   **4a.** 22 minutes

5a. 27 minutes   **6a.** 20 minutes   **7a.** 18 minutes   **8a.** 31 minutes

9a. 3 minutes   **10a.** 56 minutes   **11a.** 42 minutes   **12a.** 54 minutes

13a. 46 minutes

---

page 19
Telling the time

Time **M6**

1. 20 past 9   **2.** 5 past 4   **3.** 14 minutes to 7

4. 3 minutes past 11   **5.** 10 minutes to 3   **6.** 27 minutes past 1

7. 4 minutes to 6   **8.** 27 minutes to 12   **9.** 21 minutes past 8

● **1.** 9:20   **2.** 4:05   **3.** 6:46   **4.** 11:03   **5.** 2:50

   6. 1:27   **7.** 5:56   **8.** 11:33   **9.** 8:21

10. 27 minutes   **11.** 34 minutes   **12.** 27 minutes

---

page 20
Telling the time

Time **M6**

1. 1 and f   **2.** 2 and d   **3.** 3 and a   **4.** 4 and c   **5.** 5 and g

6. 6 and b   **7.** 7 and e

Shape, Data and Measures

Time **M6**

1. 5:35   2. 2:51   3. 4:11   4. 7:23   5. 7:04
6. 9:14   7. 5:57

8. 10 minutes + 42 minutes + 15 minutes = 67 minutes
   7:30 + 67 minutes = 8:37   Vijay gets to school at 8:37 a.m.
9. 90 minutes + 5 minutes = 95 minutes   9:10 + 95 minutes = 10:45
   Yes, Jess' film has been recorded.

page 21
a.m. and p.m.
Time **M6**

1. 7:20 a.m.   2. 11:20 a.m.   3. 3:45 p.m.   4. 1:35 p.m.
5. 4:45 a.m.   6. 12:15 a.m.   7. 2:15 p.m.

8–15. Answers will vary.

page 22
Calendars
Time **M7**

1. 6 November   2. 20 November   3. 23 November
4. 19 November

5. Sunday   6. Tuesday   7. Thursday   8. Wednesday

9. 8 days   10. 12 days   11. 16 days

page 23
Calendars
Time **M7**

1. 5   2. 4   3. 4   4. 4   5. 5

6. Tuesday   7. Monday   8. Saturday   9. Wednesday   10. Friday

11. Thursday   12. Sunday   13. Friday   14. Thursday   15. Tuesday
16. Sunday

17. January → 8   18. February → 8   19. March → 10
20. April → 8   21. May → 8   22. June → 10

Shape, Data and Measures

page 24
Calendars

January, February, March, April, May, June, July, August, September, October, November, December

1. January 31 days
2. March 31 days
3. October 31 days
4. June 30 days
5. April 30 days
6. August 31 days
7. July 31 days
8. May 31 days
9. September 30 days
10. November 30 days
11. February 28 or 29 days
12. December 31 days

page 25
Timetables

1. 10:30
2. 1:00
3. 11:30
4. 12:30
5. 9:00
6. 10:15
7. 9:50

1a. 11:30
2a. 1:10
3a. 12:30
4a. 1:00
5a. 9:20
6a. 10:30
7a. 10:15

8. Space Cops
9. Strange Hill School
10. News
11. Bonzo the Dog

@

Programme	Length
Rab and Rob	20 minutes
Bonzo the Dog	30 minutes
Strange Hill School	25 minutes
Dragon Quest	15 minutes
Animal Watch	1 hour
Space Cops	1 hour
Brainiac Quiz	30 minutes
News	10 minutes

page 26
Timetables

1. 20 minutes
2. 20 minutes
3. 3 hours 30 minutes
4. 30 minutes

5. 4 hours
6. 35 minutes
7. 7 hours 45 minutes
8. 55 minutes
9. 55 minutes

Shape, Data and Measures

page 27

Timetables

1. 5 minutes   **2.** 1 hour 16 minutes   **3.** 1 hour 37 minutes
4. 2 hours 2 minutes

5. 1 hour 5 minutes   **6.** 6 minutes   **7.** 40 minutes
8. 1 hour 10 minutes   **9.** 27 minutes   **10.** 1 hour 37 minutes
11. 46 minutes   **12.** 48 minutes

Bus station	3:30
Supermarket	3:35
School	4:40
Town hall	4:46
Post office	4:52
Library	5:04
Hospital	5:07
Train station	5:12
Swimming pool	5:32
Bus station	5:40

Explore

From	To	Time
Bus station	Supermarket	5 minutes
Supermarket	School	1 hour 5 minutes
School	Town hall	6 minutes
Town hall	Post office	6 minutes
Post office	Library	12 minutes
Library	Hospital	3 minutes
Hospital	Train station	5 minutes
Train station	Swimming pool	20 minutes
Swimming pool	Bus station	8 minutes

Shape, Data and Measures

page 27 cont ...

Times in order	From	To
3 minutes	Library	Hospital
5 minutes	Bus station	Supermarket
5 minutes	Hospital	Train station
6 minutes	Town hall	Post office
6 minutes	School	Town hall
8 minutes	Swimming pool	Bus station
12 minutes	Post office	Library
20 minutes	Train station	Swimming pool
I hour 5 minutes	Supermarket	School

The shortest journey is 3 minutes, from the library to the hospital.
The longest journey is I hour 5 minutes, from the supermarket to the school.

---

page 28
Seconds

I. 20 seconds	**2.** 10 seconds	**3.** 35 seconds	**4.** 45 seconds
5. 15 seconds	**6.** 55 seconds	**7.** 30 seconds	**8.** 17 seconds
9. 39 seconds	**10.** 5 seconds	**II.** 8 seconds	**12.** 48 seconds
13. 50 seconds			

Ia. 40 seconds	**2a.** 50 seconds	**3a.** 25 seconds	**4a.** 15 seconds
5a. 45 seconds	**6a.** 5 seconds	**7a.** 30 seconds	**8a.** 43 seconds
9a. 21 seconds	**10a.** 55 seconds	**IIa.** 52 seconds	**12a.** 12 seconds
13a. 10 seconds			

---

page 29
Seconds

I. I minute 15 seconds	**2.** I minute 32 seconds
3. I minute 50 seconds	**4.** I minute 36 seconds
5. 2 minutes 10 seconds	**6.** 2 minutes 5 seconds
7. I minute 31 seconds	**8.** 2 minutes 2 seconds
9. I minute 24 seconds	

Shape, Data and Measures

Time **M9**

10. Raj, Ben, Jess, Fi
11. Mani, Marcos
12. nobody
13. Bec, Tim
14. Jill
15. Raj
16. Ben
17. Mani

2. Raj, Jess, Ben, Fi, Mani, Marcos, Tim, Bec, Jill

---

page 30
Seconds
Time **M9**

1. 80 seconds
2. 65 seconds
3. 100 seconds
4. 67 seconds
5. 112 seconds
6. 132 seconds
7. 130 seconds
8. 95 seconds
9. 140 seconds
10. 160 seconds

11. 40 seconds — 4 points
12. 1 minute 20 seconds — 8 points
13. 1 minute 50 seconds — 11 points
14. 3 minutes — 18 points
15. 2 minutes 30 seconds — 15 points
16. 2 minutes — 12 points
17. 4 minutes 30 seconds — 27 points

Explore
5 minutes = 300 seconds
half an hour = 1800 seconds
an hour = 3600 seconds

Answers will vary.

---

page 31
Seconds
Time **M9**

1. 150 seconds
2. 55 seconds
3. 200 seconds
4. 30 seconds
5. 240 seconds
6. 10 seconds
7. 1000 seconds

8. 10 minutes = 600 seconds $600 \div 30 = 20$ $600 \div 60 = 10$
   largest number of games possible 20; fewest games possible 10
9. 600 seconds = 10 minutes; puppies born at 10:20, 10:30, 10:40, 10:50, 11:00
   last puppy born at 11:00

Shape, Data and Measures

page 32
Polygons

I.	yes	triangle	2.	yes	rectangle	
3.	yes	hexagon	4.	no	ellipse or oval	
5.	yes	pentagon	6.	yes	square	
7.	yes	hexagon	8.	no	semicircle	
9.	yes	triangle	10.	no	circle	
II.	no		12.	yes	hexagon	
13.	yes	kite or quadrilateral				

⊘ Answers as above.

---

page 33
Naming polygons

I. octagon, 8	2. square, 4	3. octagon, 8
4. pentagon, 5	5. triangle, 3	6. hexagon, 6
7. rectangle, 4	8. triangle, 3	9. heptagon, 7
10. hexagon, 6	II. hexagon, 6	12. pentagon, 5
13. rectangle, 4		

14–19. Answers will vary.

---

page 34
Naming polygons

I. pentagon, rectangle	2. square, triangle
3. hexagon, heptagon	4. hexagon, quadrilateral
5. octagon, triangle	6. heptagon, pentagon
7. triangle, hexagon	8. quadrilateral, octagon
9. pentagon, square	

10–14. Answers will vary.

---

page 35
Regular polygons

I. yes, regular hexagon	2. yes, square
3. no, triangle	4. no, hexagon
5. yes, regular (equilateral) triangle	6. no, pentagon

Shape, Data and Measures

2-d shape **S2**

7. yes, regular octagon
9. yes, regular pentagon
11. no, triangle
13 no, quadrilateral (kite)

8. no, rectangle
10. no, hexagon
12. no, octagon

Explore
Answers will vary.

---

page 36
Isosceles and equilateral triangles

2-d shape **S2**

1. equilateral
5. isosceles
9. isosceles

2. isosceles
6. equilateral
10. equilateral

3. equilateral
7. equilateral
11. equilateral

4. isosceles
8. isosceles

---

page 37
Isosceles triangles

2-d shape **S2**

1. no
6. no

2. yes
7. yes

3. no
8. no

4. no
9. no

5. yes

---

page 38
Symmetry

Symmetry **S3**

1. yes
6. no
11. no

2. no
7. yes
12. no

3. no
8. yes

4. yes
9. yes

5. yes
10. yes

Explore
Answers will vary.

Shape, Data and Measures

Symmetry

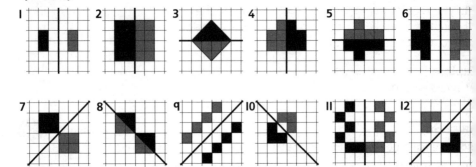

Answers will vary.

Symmetrical patterns

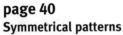
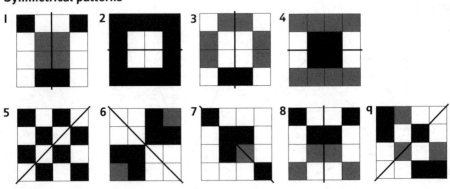

Explore
Answers will vary.

Nets

I. yes	**2.** no	**3.** yes	**4.** no	**5.** yes
6. no	**7.** yes	**8.** no	**q.** yes	

Shape, Data and Measures

page 42
Nets

3-d shape **S4**

1. cube
2. tetrahedron or triangular-based pyramid
3. cuboid
4. square-based pyramid
5. triangular prism
6. pentagonal prism
7. cuboid or square prism
8. cube
9. pentagonal-based pyramid
10. hexagonal prism

❷ Answers will vary.

1a. 6	b. 8	c. 12		2a. 4	b. 4	c. 6
3a. 6	b. 8	c. 12		4a. 5	b. 5	c. 8
5a. 5	b. 6	c. 9		6a. 7	b. 10	c. 15
7a. 6	b. 8	c. 12		8a. 6	b. 8	c. 12
9a. 6	b. 6	c. 10		10a. 8	b. 12	c. 18

page 43
Prisms and pyramids

3-d shape **S4**

1. prism
2. pyramid
3. prism
4. pyramid
5. pyramid
6. prism
7. prism
8. prism
9. pyramid
10. pyramid

2a. square-based 4a. triangular-based 5a. pentagonal-based
9a. triangular-based 10a. hexagonal-based

❷ 4 and 9 are tetrahedra

page 44
Compass points

Direction **S5**

1. east
2. south
3. south-west
4. north
5. north-east
6. west
7. south-east
8. north-east
9. north-west
10. south-east
11. south-west
12. south

1a. west
2a. north
3a. north-east
4a. south
5a. south-west
6a. east
7a. north-west
8a. south-west
9a. south-east
10a. north-west
11a. north-east
12a. north

Explore

east and west
north-east and south-west
south-east and north-west

Shape, Data and Measures

page 45
Compass points

I. south **2.** north **3.** east **4.** west
5. south-east

6. east **7.** south-east **8.** north **9.** west
10. south **II.** north-east

12. east **13.** south-west **14.** north-west **15.** west
16. north-east **17.** north

page 46
Compass points

I. north-east **2.** east **3.** north-east **4.** north
5. south **6.** north-west **7.** north-east **8.** south-west
9. south-east

⊘ Answers will vary.

Explore
Answers will vary.

page 47
Turning

I. north to south-east
2. east to north
3. west to north-east
4. south to north-west
5. south-west to east
6. south-east to north-east
7. north-west to south-east
8. north to south-east
9. south to north-east

Ia. $1\frac{1}{2}$ right angles **2a.** 3 right angles **3a.** $1\frac{1}{2}$ right angles
4a. $2\frac{1}{2}$ right angles **5a.** $1\frac{1}{2}$ right angles **6a.** 1 right angle
7a. 2 right angles **8a.** $2\frac{1}{2}$ right angles **9a.** $2\frac{1}{2}$ right angles

Shape, Data and Measures

page 48

Angles

1. north to south	2. west to north
3. north-east to south-west	4. south to north-east
5. east to north-west	6. north-west to north
7. north to west	8. south-east to north-east
9. west to north-west	10. south-west to west

1a. clockwise	2a. clockwise	3a. clockwise
4a. anticlockwise	5a. clockwise	6a. clockwise
7a. clockwise	8a. anticlockwise	9a. clockwise
10a. anticlockwise		

Explore
Answers will vary.

---

page 49

Angles

1. half past 12	2. 20 to 5	3. 8 o'clock	4. quarter to 10
5. 10 to 3	6. 10 past 5	7. half past 11	8. 10 to 10
9. 25 to 9	10. 10 to 2		

11. $1\frac{1}{3}$ right angles = 120°   12. $\frac{1}{3}$ right angle = 30°

13. 2 right angles = 180°   14. 3 right angles = 270°

15. $\frac{2}{3}$ right angle = 60°   16. $2\frac{1}{3}$ right angles = 210°

17. 1 right angle = 90°   18. $3\frac{1}{3}$ right angles = 300°

---

page 50

Coordinates

1. 5	2. 2	3. 3	4. 6	5. 0
6. 1	7. 2	8. 4	9. 5	

1a. 1	2a. 3	3a. 5	4a. 3	5a. 4
6a. 5	7a. 0	8a. 2	9a. 6	

1b. (5,1)	2b. (2,3)	3b. (3,5)	4b. (6,3)	5b. (0,4)
6b. (1,5)	7b. (2,0)	8b. (4,2)	9b. (5,6)	

Shape, Data and Measures

Coordinates

I. (I,I)	**2.** (5,5)	**3.** (8,6)	**4.** (9,9)	**5.** (9,2)
6. (2,3)	**7.** (0,4)	**8.** (5,I)	**9.** (4,7)	**10.** (2,6)

Coordinates

I. roundabout	**2.** oak tree	**3.** bench	**4.** slide
5. see-saw	**6.** pond	**7.** gate	**8.** café
9. sand pit	**10.** swings		

II. roundabout   **12.** sand pit   **13.** bench

Frequency tables

vowel	total
a	12
e	8
i	7
o	6
u	I

I. i	**2.** o	**3.** a	**4.** u	**5.** a	**6.** e

7. e, I more   **8.** e, 7 more   **9.** i, I more   **10.** o, 5 more
II. a, 4 more   **12.** a, II more

Explore
Answers will vary.

Frequency tables

I. Junior Street	**2.** Clever Class	**3.** The Odd Family
4. Animals, animals	**5.** The Odd Family	**6.** Space Cops

7. 10   **8.** 30   **9.** 15   **10.** 45   **II.** 40   **12.** 37

Explore
Answers will vary.

Shape, Data and Measures

Frequency tables

number	frequency
0	2
I	5
2	8
3	6
4	7
5	3
6	4
7	3
8	3
q	I

I. twice   **2.** 3 times   **3.** 3 times   **4.** once
5. 5 times   **6.** 2   **7.** q   **8.** I
q. 6   **10.** 3   **II.** 2   **12.** q
13. 8

Explore
Answers will vary.

Pictographs

I. April   **2.** July   **3.** 7   **4.** 21   **5.** 14   **6.** 6
7. 45   **8.** 13   **q.** 17   **10.** 8   **II.** 7

Days it didn't rain, March to July

Shape, Data and Measures

page 57
Pictographs

1. United, Rovers and Town
2. City and Rangers
3. 20 – 18 = 2   2 goals
4. 20 – 7 = 13   13 goals
5. 20 – 14 = 6   6 goals
6. 20 – 10 = 10   10 goals
7. 28 goals
8. 33 goals
9. 68 goals

Explore
Answers will vary.

---

page 58
Pictographs

1. 19
2. 15
3. 16
4. 11
5. 14
6. red, blue, black
7. yellow, pink
8. 33
9. 31
10. 64
11. 61
12. 56
13. red
14. black

Colours of sweets in a packet

Number of sweets

---

page 59
Bar graphs

1. 10
2. 0
3. 8
4. 7
5. 13
6. 10
7. 3
8. 13
9. cat, fish
10. dog, rabbit, mouse
11. dog, rabbit, hamster
12. cat, fish, hamster

Explore
Answers will vary.

Shape, Data and Measures

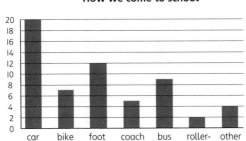

How we come to school

I. 25   2. 16   3. 14   4. 14   5. 5
6. 15   7. 11   8. 4   9. 13

I. 55   2. 40   3. 50   4. 15
5. Thursday 6. Wednesday 7. 75   8. 70
9. 90   10. 120   11. 195

I. Ben, Mandy, Sophie   2. Ben, Mandy, Rikki, Sumi
3. Ben, Mandy   4. Sophie
5. Rikki, Sumi   6. Dan, Guy
7.   8.

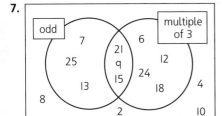
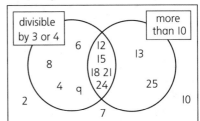

Shape, Data and Measures

Carroll diagrams

1. Jon, Suzie, Amit
2. Jon, Suzie, Karen, Sean, Ruth
3. Karen, Sean, Ruth, Matt, Beni
4. Karen, Sean, Ruth
5. Amit
6. Jon, Suzie
7. Matt, Beni

8.

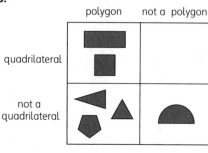

9.

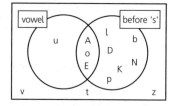

Sorting diagrams

1.

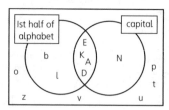

2.

	capital	not a capital
vowel	A E	u o
not a vowel	K N D	b z t v l p

3.

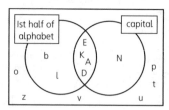

4.

	before 'j'	not before 'j'
capital	A D E	K N
not a capital	b	z t v l p u o

Explore

Answers will vary.

Photocopy Masters

Page I

4-digit numbers

I. 4372	**2.** 2679	**3.** 4852	**4.** 7374	**5.** 7562
6. 4039	**7.** 7903	**8.** 2850	**9.** 7003	**10.** 6080
II. 4552	**12.** 3974	**13.** 4516		

Page 2

Place-value N1

4-digit numbers

4265	8571	3206	4057	3980

Page 4

Addition/subtraction N2

Adding to 10 and 20

I. $1 + 9 = 10$	**2.** $3 + 7 = 10$	**3.** $4 + 6 = 10$
4. $8 + 2 = 10$	**5.** $7 + 3 = 10$	**6.** $4 + 6 = 10$
7. $0 + 10 = 10$	**8.** $1 + 9 = 10$	**9.** $8 + 2 = 10$
10. $3 + 7 = 10$	**II.** $5 + 5 = 10$	**12.** $10 + 0 = 10$
13. $9 + 11 = 20$	**14.** $15 + 5 = 20$	**15.** $12 + 8 = 20$
16. $11 + 9 = 20$	**17.** $6 + 14 = 20$	**18.** $10 + 10 = 20$
19. $8 + 12 = 20$	**20.** $18 + 2 = 20$	**21.** $13 + 7 = 20$
22. $7 + 13 = 20$	**23.** $3 + 17 = 20$	**24.** $14 + 6 = 20$

Page 6

Addition/subtraction N2

Adding to the next ten

I. $27 + 3 = 30$	**2.** $56 + 4 = 60$	**3.** $43 + 7 = 50$
4. $33 + 7 = 40$	**5.** $44 + 6 = 50$	**6.** $79 + 1 = 80$
7. $115 + 5 = 120$	**8.** $94 + 6 = 100$	**9.** $89 + 1 = 90$
10. $65 + 5 = 70$	**II.** $81 + 9 = 90$	**12.** $52 + 8 = 60$
13. $36 + 4 = 40$	**14.** $108 + 2 = 110$	**15.** $62 + 8 = 70$
16. $11 + 9 = 20$	**17.** $97 + 3 = 100$	**18.** $74 + 6 = 80$
19. $128 + 2 = 130$	**20.** $137 + 3 = 140$	

Page 7

Addition/subtraction N3

Differences

I. $121 - 117 = 4$	**2.** $112 - 106 = 6$	**3.** $134 - 129 = 5$
4. $125 - 118 = 7$	**5.** $111 - 105 = 6$	**6.** $135 - 127 = 8$
7. $124 - 119 = 5$	**8.** $122 - 116 = 6$	**9.** $143 - 137 = 6$
10. $113 - 107 = 6$	**II.** $131 - 126 = 5$	**12.** $142 - 135 = 7$

Photocopy Masters

Page 7 cont ...

13. $127 - 118 = 9$ **14.** $121 - 113 = 8$ **15.** $114 - 106 = 8$

16. $132 - 125 = 7$ **17.** $146 - 137 = 9$

Page 9

Adding to 100

$75 + 25 = 100$ $30 + 70 = 100$ $50 + 50 = 100$

$15 + 85 = 100$ $80 + 20 = 100$ $90 + 10 = 100$

$5 + 95 = 100$ $40 + 60 = 100$ $45 + 55 = 100$

$65 + 35 = 100$

Page 10

Adding to 100

1. 26 shaded + 74 unshaded = 100   **2.** 37 shaded + 63 unshaded = 100

3. 44 shaded + 56 unshaded = 100   **4.** 19 shaded + 81 unshaded = 100

5. 52 shaded + 48 unshaded = 100   **6.** 86 shaded + 14 unshaded = 100

7. 32 shaded + 68 unshaded = 100   **8.** 71 shaded + 29 unshaded = 100

Page 11

Adding to 100

1. $23 + 77 = 100$ **2.** $80 + 20 = 100$ **3.** $51 + 49 = 100$

4. $64 + 36 = 100$ **5.** $81 + 19 = 100$ **6.** $64 + 36 = 100$

7. $35 + 65 = 100$ **8.** $55 + 45 = 100$ **9.** $8 + 92 = 100$

10. $69 + 31 = 100$ **11.** $53 + 47 = 100$ **12.** $70 + 30 = 100$

13. $72 + 28 = 100$ **14.** $93 + 7 = 100$ **15.** $56 + 44 = 100$

16. $82 + 18 = 100$ **17.** $29 + 71 = 100$ **18.** $28 + 72 = 100$

Page 13

Adding several numbers

9	3	5	7	2	26
6	5	4	9	1	25
5	2	8	3	8	26
3	7	9	6	5	30
9	8	6	4	7	34
32	25	32	29	23	

Photocopy Masters

7	9	5	13	9	(43)
4	9	8	6	12	(39)
5	11	3	9	7	(35)
9	8	12	7	13	(49)
6	9	7	11	4	(37)

(31) (46) (35) (46) (45)

Page 14   Properties of number   N6
Counting in Is, 10s, 25s and 50s

1. 50	60	70	80	**2.** 350	400	450	500
3. 150	125	100	75	**4.** 168	169	170	171
5. 600	550	500	450	**6.** 225	250	275	300
7. 180	179	178	177	**8.** 550	650	750	850
9. 322	372	422	472	**10.** 760	710	660	610

Page 15   Properties of number   N6
Counting

Answers will vary.

Page 16   Multiplication/division   N7
Multiplying

1. A and F $3 \times 5 = 5 \times 3 = 15$
2. B and H $3 \times 7 = 7 \times 3 = 21$
3. C and I $2 \times 9 = 9 \times 2 = 18$
4. D and J $8 \times 4 = 4 \times 8 = 32$
5. E and G $4 \times 6 = 6 \times 4 = 24$

Page 17   Multiplication/division   N7
Multiplying

1. $2 \times 30 = 60$, $30 \times 2 = 60$
2. $4 \times 20 = 80$, $20 \times 4 = 80$
3. $3 \times 40 = 120$, $40 \times 3 = 120$
4. $5 \times 20 = 100$, $20 \times 5 = 100$
5. $4 \times 25 = 100$, $25 \times 4 = 100$
6. $3 \times 20 = 60$, $20 \times 3 = 60$

Photocopy Masters

Page 17 cont ...

 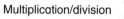

7. 2 x 40 = 80, 40 x 2 = 80
9. 2 x 60 = 120, 60 x 2 = 120
11. 6 x 25 = 150, 25 x 6 = 150

8. 4 x 30 = 120, 30 x 4 = 120
10. 3 x 50 = 150, 50 x 3 = 150
12. 5 x 40 = 200, 40 x 5 = 200

Page 18
Dividing

1. 12 ÷ 2 = 6
4. 10 ÷ 5 = 2
7. 15 ÷ 5 = 3

2. 15 ÷ 3 = 5
5. 27 ÷ 3 = 9
8. 30 ÷ 5 = 6

3. 16 ÷ 4 = 4
6. 20 ÷ 2 = 10
9. 20 ÷ 5 = 4

Page 19
Dividing

1. 12 ÷ 2 = 6
4. 10 ÷ 5 = 2
7. 40 ÷ 8 = 5
10. 16 ÷ 4 = 4
13. 24 ÷ 8 = 3
16. 18 ÷ 6 = 3
19. 20 ÷ 4 = 5

2. 15 ÷ 3 = 5
5. 12 ÷ 6 = 2
8. 16 ÷ 2 = 8
11. 9 ÷ 3 = 3
14. 8 ÷ 2 = 4
17. 30 ÷ 3 = 10
20. 35 ÷ 7 = 5

3. 8 ÷ 4 = 2
6. 21 ÷ 7 = 3
9. 50 ÷ 10 = 5
12. 18 ÷ 9 = 2
15. 15 ÷ 5 = 3
18. 90 ÷ 10 = 9

Page 20
Problem page

1. 32 ÷ 4 = 8   8 biscuits
2. 48 ÷ 6 = 8   8 rows
3. 45 ÷ 5 = 9   9 piles
4. 1 pile of 28   2 piles of 14   14 piles of 2   4 piles of 7   7 piles of 4
5. 3 x 6 = 18   18
6. 2 (32) or 6 (36)
7. 12 or 24
8. 5 x 6 = 30   30 marbles

Page 21
Threes and fours

● 12, 24, 36, 48, 60

Photocopy Masters

5	12	9
8	10	6
11	7	13

31	14	41
25	32	21
12	24	33

16	44	35
42	32	26
37	28	19

17 pairs

1, 2   2, 4   3, 6   4, 8   5, 10   6, 12   7, 14   8, 16   9, 18   13, 26   14, 28   15, 30
16, 32   17, 34   18, 36   19, 38   23, 46

1	2	3	4	5	6	7	8	9	10
11	12	13	14	15	16	17	18	19	20
21	22	23	24	25	26	27	28	29	30
31	32	33	34	35	36	37	38	39	40
41	42	43	44	45	46	47	48	49	50
51	52	53	54	55	56	57	58	59	60
61	62	63	64	65	66	67	68	69	70
71	72	73	74	75	76	77	78	79	80
81	82	83	84	85	86	87	88	89	90
91	92	93	94	95	96	97	98	99	100

Answers will vary.

Photocopy Masters

Page 28

Fours and eights

1. 10 x 8 = 80
2. 9 x 8 = 72
3. 5 x 4 = 20   5 x 8 = 40
4. 7 x 4 = 28   7 x 8 = 56
5. 20 x 8 = 160
6. 30 x 8 = 240
7. 15 x 8 = 120
8. 100 x 4 = 400   100 x 8 = 800
9. 14 x 8 = 112
10. 25 x 8 = 200

Page 29
Fractions

1. shaded $\frac{5}{6}$, clear $\frac{1}{6}$
2. shaded $\frac{3}{4}$, clear $\frac{1}{4}$
3. shaded $\frac{1}{3}$, clear $\frac{2}{3}$
4. shaded $\frac{3}{8}$, clear $\frac{5}{8}$
5. shaded $\frac{4}{6}$, clear $\frac{2}{6}$
6. shaded $\frac{3}{12}$, clear $\frac{9}{12}$
7. shaded $\frac{7}{8}$, clear $\frac{1}{8}$
8. shaded $\frac{4}{9}$, clear $\frac{5}{9}$

Page 30
Fractions

Answers will vary.

Page 31
Fractions

1. $\frac{3}{8}$ 2. $\frac{6}{8}$ 3. $\frac{3}{8}$ 4. $\frac{5}{8}$ 5. $\frac{2}{8}$
6. $\frac{5}{8}$ 7. $\frac{4}{8}$ 8. $\frac{2}{8}$ 9. $\frac{4}{8}$ 10. $\frac{3}{8}$

Page 32

Matching fractions

1. $\frac{1}{2} = \frac{2}{4}$ 2. $\frac{1}{3} = \frac{2}{6}$ 3. $\frac{2}{3} = \frac{4}{6}$ 4. $\frac{1}{4} = \frac{2}{8}$
5. $\frac{1}{2} = \frac{3}{6}$ 6. $\frac{3}{4} = \frac{6}{8}$ 7. $\frac{3}{5} = \frac{6}{10}$ 8. $\frac{1}{2} = \frac{4}{8}$

Photocopy Masters

Fractions/decimals **N13**

Matching fractions

1. $\frac{1}{2} = \frac{2}{4}$
2. $1 = \frac{4}{4}$
3. $\frac{1}{2} = \frac{4}{8}$
4. $\frac{1}{8} = \frac{2}{16}$
5. $\frac{8}{8} = 1$
6. $\frac{2}{4} = \frac{4}{8}$
7. $\frac{4}{16} = \frac{1}{4}$
8. $\frac{1}{4} = \frac{2}{8}$
9. $\frac{1}{2} = \frac{8}{16}$
10. $\frac{2}{2} = 1$
11. $\frac{3}{4} = \frac{6}{8}$
12. $\frac{3}{4} = \frac{12}{16}$

Fractions/decimals **N13**

Matching fractions

13 pairs

$\frac{1}{2} = \frac{2}{4} = \frac{3}{6} = \frac{4}{8} = \frac{5}{10}$

$\frac{1}{4} = \frac{2}{8}$

$\frac{2}{3} = \frac{4}{6} = \frac{6}{9}$

$\frac{3}{5} = \frac{6}{10}$

$\frac{1}{3} = \frac{2}{6} = \frac{3}{9}$

$\frac{1}{5} = \frac{2}{10}$

$\frac{2}{5} = \frac{4}{10}$

$\frac{4}{5} = \frac{8}{10}$

Addition/subtraction **N14**

Adding near multiples of 10

+	26	41	17	52	33	67
19	45	60	36	71	52	86
12	38	53	29	64	45	79
39	65	80	56	91	72	106
21	47	62	38	73	54	88

+	252	173	86	345	64	147
31	283	204	117	376	95	178
49	301	222	135	394	113	196
22	274	195	108	367	86	169
59	311	232	145	404	123	206

Addition/subtraction **N14**

Problem page

1. $83p - 19p = 64p$
2. $132 + 9 = 141$ pages
3. $£22 + £29 = £51$
4. $235 + 39 + 22 = 296$ points
5. $44 - 29 = 15$ 15 years old
6. $72 + 19 = 91$
7. $90 - 29 - 43 = 18$
8. 10:51 a.m.

Photocopy Masters

Page 37

Adding and subtracting multiples of 10

1. $60 + 30 = 90$
2. $70 - 20 = 50$
3. $120 + 50 = 170$
4. $160 - 40 = 120$
5. $270 - 30 = 240$
6. $70 + 210 = 280$
7. $250 - 120 = 130$
8. $130 + 140 = 270$
9. $320 + 140 = 460$
10. $670 - 340 = 330$
11. $80 + 70 = 150$
12. $130 - 60 = 70$
13. $150 + 90 = 240$
14. $220 - 70 = 150$
15. $370 + 140 = 510$
16. $530 - 270 = 260$

Page 38

Adding and subtracting multiples of 10

1. $200 + 300 = 500$
2. $900 - 500 = 400$
3. $1400 + 500 = 1900$
4. $1700 - 300 = 1400$
5. $300 + 2400 = 2700$
6. $2600 - 400 = 2200$
7. $4600 - 1500 = 3100$
8. $3500 + 1300 = 4800$
9. $5200 + 2400 = 7600$
10. $7700 - 3500 = 4200$
11. $1200 - 700 = 500$
12. $700 + 800 = 1500$
13. $2500 + 600 = 3100$
14. $3100 - 700 = 2400$
15. $6200 - 1700 = 4500$
16. $4800 + 1500 = 6300$

Page 39

4-digit numbers

1. 2553 2563 2573
2. 4261 4271 4281
3. 6849 6859 6869
4. 3510 3520 3530
5. 5393 5403 5413
6. 7018 7028 7038
7. 3997 4007 4017
8. 3582 3592 3602
9. 3961 3971 3981
10. 2689 2699 2709

Photocopy Masters

4-digit numbers

Place-value N16

	I less	10 more	100 less	1000 more
3728	3727	3738	3628	4728
5462	5461	5472	5362	6462
7531	7530	7541	7431	8531
4089	4088	4099	3989	5089
2971	2970	2981	2871	3971
3296	3295	3306	3196	4296
2504	2503	2514	2404	3504
3098	3097	3108	2998	4098
9501	9500	9511	9401	10501
2309	2308	2319	2209	3309
4095	4094	4105	3995	5095
6200	6199	6210	6100	7200

Adding

Addition/subtraction N17

1. $23 + 15 + 31 = 69$
2. $26 + 32 + 14 = 72$
3. $17 + 25 + 34 = 76$
4. $46 + 18 + 25 = 89$
5. $42 + 37 + 9 = 88$
6. $15 + 28 + 17 = 60$
7. $52 + 16 + 23 = 91$
8. $35 + 21 + 29 = 85$
9. $52 + 46 + 37 = 135$
10. $48 + 63 + 59 = 170$

Adding

Addition/subtraction N17

1. $23 + 31 + 24 = 16 + 27 + 35 = 78$
2. $15 + 16 + 27 = 58$
3. $23 + 16 + 24 = 63$
4. $31 + 42 + 35 = 108$
5. $24 + 27 + 35 = 86$
6. $23 + 15 + 31 = 69$
7. $23 + 24 + 35 = 31 + 16 + 35 = 31 + 24 + 27 = 82$

Photocopy Masters

Page 44
Adding

1. $7 + 10 = 17$
2. $18 + 10 = 28$
3. $25 + 10 = 35$
4. $34 + 10 = 44$
5. $72 + 10 = 82$
6. $23 + 10 = 33$
7. $46 + 10 = 56$
8. $37 + 10 = 47$
9. $58 + 10 = 68$
10. $89 + 10 = 99$
11. $16 + 20 = 36$
12. $27 + 20 = 47$
13. $9 + 20 = 29$
14. $35 + 20 = 55$
15. $43 + 20 = 63$
16. $79 + 20 = 99$
17. $38 + 20 = 58$
18. $52 + 20 = 72$
19. $64 + 20 = 84$
20. $85 + 20 = 105$

Page 45
Adding

1. $235 + 40 = 275$
2. $326 + 20 = 346$
3. $426 + 30 = 456$
4. $635 + 50 = 685$
5. $615 + 60 = 675$
6. $346 + 20 = 366$
7. $245 + 10 = 255$
8. $954 + 30 = 984$
9. $532 + 60 = 592$
10. $183 + 10 = 193$
11. $928 + 50 = 978$
12. $715 + 80 = 795$
13. $251 + 40 = 291$
14. $305 + 40 = 345$
15. $763 + 20 = 783$
16. $542 + 30 = 572$
17. $854 + 10 = 864$
18. $109 + 70 = 179$
19. $429 + 30 = 459$
20. $858 + 20 = 878$

Page 46
Subtracting

1. $50p - 32p = 18p$
2. $50p - 27p = 23p$
3. $50p - 8p = 42p$
4. $50p - 42p = 8p$
5. $50p - 16p = 34p$
6. $50p - 21p = 29p$
7. $50p - 39p = 11p$
8. $50p - 15p = 35p$

Page 47
Subtracting

1. $23 - 15 = 8$
2. $32 - 16 = 16$
3. $41 - 24 = 17$
4. $54 - 36 = 18$
5. $65 - 58 = 7$
6. $73 - 41 = 32$
7. $84 - 53 = 31$
8. $95 - 62 = 33$
9. $36 - 29 = 7$
10. $42 - 35 = 7$
11. $75 - 68 = 7$
12. $29 - 17 = 12$
13. $86 - 43 = 43$
14. $52 - 19 = 33$
15. $64 - 49 = 15$
16. $31 - 16 = 15$
17. $92 - 59 = 33$
18. $44 - 18 = 26$
19. $55 - 39 = 16$
20. $71 - 28 = 43$

Photocopy Masters

Subtracting

1. $21 - 13 = 8$
2. $83 - 6 = 77$
3. $42 - 37 = 5$
4. $51 - 45 = 6$
5. $72 - 58 = 14$
6. $74 - 65 = 9$
7. $80 - 66 = 14$
8. $93 - 78 = 15$
9. $63 - 38 = 25$
10. $42 - 8 = 34$
11. $72 - 47 = 25$
12. $35 - 16 = 19$
13. $31 - 9 = 22$
14. $84 - 48 = 36$
15. $54 - 29 = 25$
16. $61 - 7 = 54$
17. $65 - 8 = 57$
18. $83 - 29 = 54$
19. $94 - 35 = 59$
20. $122 - 86 = 36$

Problem page

1. $46 - 19 = 27$ 27 marbles
2. $38 - 21 = 17$ 17 years old
3. $46 - 7 = 39$ 39 days
4. $54 - 28 = 26$ 26 days
5. $33 - 16 = 17$ 17 girls
6. $52 - 19 = 33$ 33 weeks
7. $33 + 9 = 42$ half of $42 = 21$ the number is 21
8. 23 and 9

Threes and fours

1. 3	6	9	12	15	18	21	24	27	30
2. 12	15	18	21	24	27	30	33	36	39
3. 27	30	33	36	39	42	45	48	51	54
4. 4	8	12	16	20	24	28	32	36	40
5. 20	24	28	32	36	40	44	48	52	56
6. 30	27	24	21	18	15	12	9	6	3
7. 40	36	32	28	24	20	16	12	8	4
8. 32	36	40	44	48	52	56	60	64	68
9. 54	51	48	45	42	39	36	33	30	27
10. 52	48	44	40	36	32	28	24	20	16

Multiples

1. $27 \rightarrow 30$
2. $42 \rightarrow 50$
3. $56 \rightarrow 60$
4. $15 \rightarrow 20$
5. $92 \rightarrow 100$
6. $134 \rightarrow 140$
7. $7 \rightarrow 9$
8. $26 \rightarrow 27$
9. $31 \rightarrow 33$
10. $45 \rightarrow 48$
11. $17 \rightarrow 18$
12. $42 \rightarrow 45$
13. $14 \rightarrow 15$
14. $26 \rightarrow 30$
15. $31 \rightarrow 35$
16. $45 \rightarrow 50$
17. $17 \rightarrow 20$
18. $42 \rightarrow 45$
19. $6 \rightarrow 8$
20. $18 \rightarrow 20$
21. $31 \rightarrow 32$
22. $24 \rightarrow 28$
23. $37 \rightarrow 40$
24. $21 \rightarrow 24$

Photocopy Masters

Page 52
Sixes

1	2	3	4	5	6	7	8	9	10
11	12	13	14	15	16	17	18	19	20
21	22	23	24	25	26	27	28	29	30
31	32	33	34	35	36	37	38	39	40
41	42	43	44	45	46	47	48	49	50
51	52	53	54	55	56	57	58	59	60
61	62	63	64	65	66	67	68	69	70
71	72	73	74	75	76	77	78	79	80
81	82	83	84	85	86	87	88	89	90
91	92	93	94	95	96	97	98	99	100

Answers will vary.

Page 53
Threes and sixes

1. $2 \times 3 = 6$
2. $1 \times 6 = 6$
3. $4 \times 6 = 24$
4. $5 \times 3 = 15$
5. $7 \times 3 = 21$
6. $5 \times 6 = 30$
7. $8 \times 6 = 48$
8. $2 \times 6 = 12$
9. $8 \times 3 = 24$
10. $1 \times 3 = 3$
11. $7 \times 6 = 42$
12. $10 \times 6 = 60$
13. $3 \times 3 = 9$
14. $10 \times 3 = 30$
15. $9 \times 3 = 27$
16. $6 \times 6 = 36$
17. $3 \times 6 = 18$
18. $4 \times 3 = 12$
19. $6 \times 3 = 18$
20. $9 \times 6 = 54$

Photocopy Masters

Nines

1	2	3	4	5	6	7	8	9	10
11	12	13	14	15	16	17	18	19	20
21	22	23	24	25	26	27	28	29	30
31	32	33	34	35	36	37	38	39	40
41	42	43	44	45	46	47	48	49	50
51	52	53	54	55	56	57	58	59	60
61	62	63	64	65	66	67	68	69	70
71	72	73	74	75	76	77	78	79	80
81	82	83	84	85	86	87	88	89	90
91	92	93	94	95	96	97	98	99	100

Answers will vary.

Patterns in nines

1. 27	**2.** 36	**3.** 18	**4.** 81	**5.** 54	**6.** 72
7. 45	**8.** 54	**9.** 90	**10.** 63	**11.** 27	**12.** 72
13. 81	**14.** 45	**15.** 63	**16.** 36	**17.** 108	**18.** 99

Sevens

1. $2 \times 7 = 14$	**2.** $5 \times 7 = 35$	**3.** $1 \times 7 = 7$	**4.** $6 \times 7 = 42$
5. $4 \times 7 = 28$	**6.** $10 \times 7 = 70$	**7.** $8 \times 7 = 56$	**8.** $3 \times 7 = 21$
9. $9 \times 7 = 63$	**10.** $7 \times 7 = 49$	**11.** $7 \div 7 = 1$	**12.** $28 \div 7 = 4$
13. $42 \div 7 = 6$	**14.** $70 \div 7 = 10$	**15.** $21 \div 7 = 3$	**16.** $49 \div 7 = 7$
17. $63 \div 7 = 9$	**18.** $21 \div 7 = 3$	**19.** $35 \div 7 = 5$	**20.** $56 \div 7 = 8$

Photocopy Masters

Sixes and sevens

@   42

Page 60
Multiplication table

x 1	1	2	3	4	5	6	7	8	9	10
x 2	2	4	6	8	10	12	14	16	18	20
x 3	3	6	9	12	15	18	21	24	27	30
x 4	4	8	12	16	20	24	28	32	36	40
x 5	5	10	15	20	25	30	35	40	45	50
x 6	6	12	18	24	30	36	42	48	54	60
x 7	7	14	21	28	35	42	49	56	63	70
x 8	8	16	24	32	40	48	56	64	72	80
x 9	9	18	27	36	45	54	63	72	81	90
x 10	10	20	30	40	50	60	70	80	90	100

Page 62
Multiplying and dividing by 10 and 100

1. $17 \times 10 = 170$
2. $60 \div 10 = 6$
3. $90 \times 10 = 900$
4. $140 \div 10 = 14$
5. $27 \times 100 = 2700$
6. $8000 \div 100 = 80$
7. $37 \times 100 = 3700$
8. $2400 \div 100 = 24$
9. $42 \times 10 = 420$
10. $1300 \div 100 = 13$
11. $250 \div 10 = 25$
12. $16 \times 100 = 1600$

Page 63
Multiplying

Answers will vary.

Photocopy Masters

Multiplying
Multiplication/division **N26**

1. $3 \times 24 = 60 + 12 = 72$
2. $4 \times 32 = 120 + 8 = 128$
3. $5 \times 25 = 100 + 25 = 125$
4. $4 \times 42 = 160 + 8 = 168$
5. $6 \times 17 = 60 + 42 = 102$
6. $2 \times 34 = 60 + 8 = 68$
7. $5 \times 28 = 100 + 40 = 140$
8. $6 \times 34 = 180 + 24 = 204$

Page 65
Fractions
Fractions/decimals **N27**

1. $\frac{1}{4}$ $\frac{3}{4}$
2. $\frac{1}{3}$ $\frac{2}{3}$
3. $\frac{1}{6}$ $\frac{3}{6} = \frac{1}{2}$ $\frac{5}{6}$
4. $\frac{2}{5}$ $\frac{3}{5}$
5. $\frac{1}{8}$ $\frac{3}{8}$ $\frac{5}{8}$ $\frac{6}{8} = \frac{3}{4}$
6. $\frac{3}{10}$ $\frac{4}{10} = \frac{2}{5}$ $\frac{7}{10}$ $\frac{9}{10}$

Page 66
Ordering fractions
Fractions/decimals **N27**

1. $\frac{1}{3} < \frac{1}{2}$
2. $\frac{1}{5} < \frac{1}{4}$
3. $\frac{3}{8} > \frac{1}{4}$
4. $\frac{1}{2} > \frac{2}{5}$
5. $\frac{5}{8} > \frac{1}{2}$
6. $\frac{1}{4} = \frac{2}{8}$
7. $\frac{4}{5} > \frac{4}{6}$
8. $\frac{6}{8} = \frac{3}{4}$
9. $\frac{1}{6} > \frac{1}{8}$
10. $\frac{2}{3} < \frac{3}{4}$
11. $\frac{5}{8} > \frac{3}{5}$
12. $\frac{2}{3} > \frac{1}{3}$
13. $\frac{4}{6} = \frac{2}{3}$
14. $\frac{4}{5} < \frac{7}{8}$
15. $\frac{4}{8} > \frac{2}{5}$

Page 68
Fractions
Fractions/decimals **N28**

1. $\frac{1}{2}$ of $8 = 4$
2. $\frac{1}{3}$ of $9 = 3$
3. $\frac{1}{4}$ of $12 = 3$
4. $\frac{1}{5}$ of $10 = 2$
5. $\frac{1}{6}$ of $6 = 1$
6. $\frac{1}{8}$ of $8 = 1$
7. $\frac{2}{3}$ of $6 = 4$
8. $\frac{3}{4}$ of $8 = 6$
9. $\frac{2}{5}$ of $10 = 4$
10. $\frac{3}{3}$ of $6 = 6$
11. $\frac{3}{5}$ of $20 = 12$
12. $\frac{1}{2}$ of $12 = 6$
13. $\frac{3}{4}$ of $12 = 9$
14. $\frac{2}{3}$ of $9 = 6$
15. $\frac{4}{5}$ of $15 = 12$
16. $\frac{1}{6}$ of $12 = 2$
17. $\frac{5}{6}$ of $12 = 10$
18. $\frac{1}{4}$ of $16 = 4$
19. $\frac{3}{4}$ of $16 = 12$
20. $\frac{1}{5}$ of $50 = 10$

Photocopy Masters

Page 69

Rounding

A 424 → 420   B 434 → 430   C 431 → 430   D 421 → 420
E 437 → 440   F 439 → 440   G 425 → 430   H 428 → 430
I 774 → 770   J 766 → 770   K 775 → 780   L 762 → 760
M 778 → 780   N 761 → 760   O 771 → 770   P 770 → 770

Page 71

Rounding

1. 634
2. 493
3. 346 or 349
4. 639 or 643
5. 934
6. 946
7. 469
8. 396
9. 394
10. 463
11. 936 or 943
12. 693 or 694
13. 649
14. 369
15. 436 or 439
16. 496
17. 364
18. 963 or 964

Page 72

Adding

1. $352 + 47 = 399$
2. $464 + 28 = 492$
3. $537 + 84 = 621$
4. $127 + 346 = 473$
5. $258 + 463 = 721$
6. $725 + 149 = 874$
7. $358 + 462 = 820$
8. $723 + 159 = 882$
9. $271 + 436 = 707$
10. $852 + 109 = 961$
11. $203 + 598 = 801$
12. $438 + 159 = 597$

Page 74

Adding 3-digit numbers

1. $317 + 503 = 820$
2. $174 + 216 = 390$
3. $503 + 216 = 719$
4. $428 + 503 = 931$
5. $317 + 174 = 491$
6. $295 + 503 = 798$
7. $428 + 174 = 602$
8. $428 + 216 = 644$
9. $295 + 317 = 612$

Page 75

Subtracting multiples of 10

1. $82 - 30 = 52$
2. $47 - 20 = 27$
3. $165 - 50 = 115$
4. $258 - 40 = 218$

Photocopy Masters

5. 143 – 60 = 83
7. 425 – 30 = 395
9. 537 – 70 = 467
11. 207 – 40 = 167
3. 423 – 60 = 363
5. 625 – 90 = 535
7. 320 – 70 = 250
9. 817 – 30 = 787

6. 237 – 70 = 167
8. 318 – 50 = 268
10. 108 – 80 = 28
12. 356 – 70 = 286
14. 712 – 50 = 662
16. 839 – 80 = 759
18. 540 – 80 = 460
20. 905 – 20 = 885

Page 76   Addition/subtraction   N32
Subtracting

1. 134 – 65 = 69
2. 152 – 86 = 66
3. 124 – 77 = 47
4. 186 – 98 = 88
5. 213 – 156 = 57
6. 325 – 178 = 147
7. 232 – 57 = 175
8. 241 – 85 = 156
9. 356 – 178 = 178

Page 77   Addition/subtraction   N33
Subtracting

1. 756 – 214 = 542
2. 947 – 323 = 624
3. 685 – 462 = 223
4. 892 – 551 = 341
5. 534 – 322 = 212
6. 383 – 171 = 212
7. 468 – 235 = 233
8. 565 – 443 = 122
9. 276 – 132 = 144
10. 627 – 516 = 111
11. 879 – 364 = 515
12. 754 – 621 = 133

Page 78   Addition/subtraction   N33
Subtracting

1. 729 – 387 = 342
2. 638 – 265 = 373
3. 846 – 492 = 354
4. 945 – 573 = 372
5. 534 – 281 = 253
6. 624 – 292 = 332
7. 835 – 382 = 453
8. 719 – 156 = 563

Page 79   Addition/subtraction   N33
Subtracting

Answers will vary.

Photocopy Masters

Page 80
Odds and evens

1. 75 745	**2.** 54 574	**3.** 74 754	**4.** 45 457
5. 93 963	**6.** 36 396	**7.** 96 936	**8.** 39 369
9. 81 841	**10.** 14 148	**11.** 84 814	**12.** 41 481

Page 81
Odds and evens

1. odd + odd = even
2. odd + even = odd
3. even + odd = odd
4. even + even = even
5. odd – odd = even
6. even – even = even
7. odd – even = odd
8. even – odd = odd
9. odd + odd + even = even
10. even + odd + even = odd
11. odd + even + even = odd
12. even + even + even = even
13. odd + odd + odd = odd
14. odd + even + odd = even
15. odd + odd – even = even
16. even + odd – even = odd
17. odd + even – odd = even
18. even – odd – even = odd

Page 82
Negative numbers

1. 10 °C	**2.** 2 °C	**3.** ⁻3 °C	**4.** 3 °C	**5.** ⁻6 °C
6. 3 °C	**7.** ⁻1 °C	**8.** 0 °C	**9.** 3 °C	**10.** 6 °C
11. ⁻4 °C	**12.** 7 °C	**13.** ⁻2 °C	**14.** ⁻18 °C	

Page 83
Doubling

1. $10 + 60 = 70$	**2.** $30 + 40 = 70$	**3.** $50 + 80 = 130$
4. $20 + 140 = 160$	**5.** $40 + 100 = 140$	**6.** $30 + 160 = 190$
7. $50 + 120 = 170$	**8.** $40 + 20 = 60$	

Answers will vary.

Page 84
Halving
Answers will vary.

Photocopy Masters

Doubling and halving

140 → 280		420 → 210
360 → 720		860 → 430
270 → 540		630 → 315
190 → 380		290 → 145
480 → 960		350 → 175
1300 → 2600		4200 → 2100
2400 → 4800		6800 → 3400
3600 → 7200		2700 → 1350
4700 → 9400		8500 → 4250
1900 → 3800		3900 → 1950

Multiplying

1. 25 x 3 = 75   **2.** 31 x 2 = 62   **3.** 42 x 4 = 168
4. 24 x 2 = 48   **5.** 35 x 3 = 105   **6.** 52 x 4 = 208
7. 54 x 3 = 162   **8.** 33 x 4 = 132   **9.** 62 x 5 = 310

Multiplying

Answers will vary.

Dividing

1. 16 ÷ 3 = 5 r 1   **2.** 12 ÷ 5 = 2 r 2   **3.** 15 ÷ 4 = 3 r 3
4. 17 ÷ 2 = 8 r 1   **5.** 26 ÷ 6 = 4 r 2   **6.** 19 ÷ 2 = 9 r 1
7. 30 ÷ 7 = 4 r 2   **8.** 50 ÷ 9 = 5 r 5   **9.** 23 ÷ 5 = 4 r 3
10. 26 ÷ 8 = 3 r 2   **11.** 19 ÷ 4 = 4 r 3   **12.** 18 ÷ 7 = 2 r 4
13. 16 ÷ 6 = 2 r 4   **14.** 29 ÷ 3 = 9 r 2   **15.** 54 ÷ 5 = 10 r 4
16. 38 ÷ 4 = 9 r 2

Problem page

1. 14 ÷ 3 = 4 r 2   4 cakes each, 2 left over
2. 50 ÷ 6 = 8 r 2   8 stickers
3. 5 x 7 = 35   35 + 3 = 38   38 children

Photocopy Masters

4. $42 \div 5 = 8 \text{ r } 2$ 8 stamps, 2p left
5. $34 \div 6 = 5 \text{ r } 4$ 5 full boxes
6. $30 \div 4 = 7 \text{ r } 2$ 8 boats
7. 23
8. 4, 11, 22 or 44

Page 90   Multiplication/division N39
Dividing

1. $2\overline{)34} = 17$ **2.** $3\overline{)42} = 14$ **3.** $4\overline{)56} = 14$
4. $5\overline{)75} = 15$ **5.** $6\overline{)84} = 14$ **6.** $3\overline{)51} = 17$
7. $2\overline{)46} = 23$ **8.** $4\overline{)68} = 17$ **9.** $8\overline{)96} = 12$
10. $7\overline{)84} = 12$ **11.** $3\overline{)72} = 24$ **12.** $4\overline{)88} = 22$

Page 91   Fractions/decimals N40
Tenths

1. $2\frac{2}{10}$ and $2 \cdot 2$ **2.** $1\frac{4}{10}$ and $1 \cdot 4$ **3.** $3\frac{7}{10}$ and $3 \cdot 7$ **4.** $1\frac{9}{10}$ and $1 \cdot 9$
5. $2\frac{5}{10}$ and $2 \cdot 5$ **6.** $\frac{6}{10}$ and $0 \cdot 6$ **7.** $3\frac{2}{10}$ and $3 \cdot 2$ **8.** $2\frac{1}{10}$ and $2 \cdot 1$
9. $1\frac{2}{10}$ and $1 \cdot 2$ **10.** $3\frac{5}{10}$ and $3 \cdot 5$

Page 92   Fractions/decimals N40
Tenths

$1 \cdot 3 = 1\frac{3}{10}$ $\frac{5}{10} = 0 \cdot 5$ $2\frac{4}{10} = 2 \cdot 4$ $0 \cdot 9 = \frac{9}{10}$ $3\frac{5}{10} = 3 \cdot 5$
$4 \cdot 3 = 4\frac{3}{10}$ $1 \cdot 7 = 1\frac{7}{10}$ $1\frac{1}{10} = 1 \cdot 1$ $3 \cdot 6 = 3\frac{6}{10}$

$0 \cdot 5, \quad 0 \cdot 9, \quad 1 \cdot 1, \quad 1 \cdot 3, \quad 1 \cdot 7, \quad 2 \cdot 4, \quad 3 \cdot 5, \quad 3 \cdot 6, \quad 4 \cdot 3$

Page 93   Fractions/decimals N40
Tenths

1. E   **2.** D   **3.** H   **4.** B   **5.** G   **6.** A
7. K   **8.** J   **9.** C   **10.** I   **11.** L   **12.** F

Photocopy Masters

Hundredths

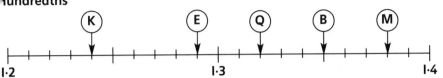

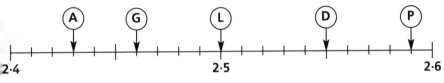

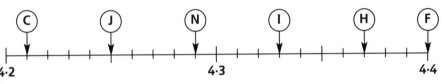

Page 95
Fractions/decimals   N41

Hundredths

1. £1·22   2. £3·15   3. £0·91   4. £4·50   5. £2·72   6. £1·55
7. £3·51   8. £1·10   9. £2·01   10. £6·25   11. £5·54   12. £10·07

Page 96
Addition/subtraction   N42

Subtracting

1. $762 - 219 = 543$ 2. $384 - 168 = 216$ 3. $686 - 159 = 527$
4. $943 - 536 = 407$ 5. $471 - 324 = 147$ 6. $565 - 257 = 308$
7. $837 - 418 = 419$ 8. $572 - 445 = 127$

Page 97
Addition/subtraction   N43

Adding and subtracting decimals

1. $£2·30 + £1·60 = £3·90$ 2. $£4·50 + £2·30 = £6·80$
3. $£4·50 + £4·25 = £8·75$ 4. $£5·45 + £1·85 = £7·30$
5. $£2·30 + £3·75 = £6·05$ 6. $£4·50 + £1·85 = £6·35$
7. $£4·50 - £2·30 = £2·20$ 8. $£2·30 - £1·60 = £0·70$
9. $£5·45 - £4·50 = £0·95$ 10. $£4·25 - £1·85 = £2·40$
11. $£3·75 - £2·30 = £1·45$ 12. $£4·50 - £4·25 = £0·25$

Photocopy Masters

Page 98

Centimetres

Estimates will vary.

a	b	c	d	e	f	g	h
16 cm	12 cm	17 cm	3 cm	4 cm	10 cm	4 cm	15 cm

Page 99

Millimetres, centimetres, metres and kilometres

1. 1 cm = 10 mm
2. 1 cm 7 mm = 17mm
3. $\frac{1}{2}$ cm = 5 mm
4. 5 cm = 50 mm
5. 3 cm = 35 mm
6. 1 m = 1000mm
7. 1 m = 100 cm
8. 1m 20 cm = 120 cm
9. 60 mm = 6 cm
10. $\frac{1}{4}$ m = 25 cm
11. 35 mm = 3·5 cm
12. 2m 50cm = 250 cm
13. 100 cm = 1 m
14. 1 km = 1000 m
15. 600 cm = 6 m
16. 1000 cm = 10 m
17. $\frac{1}{2}$ km = 500 m
18. 1000 mm = 1m
19. 1000 m = 1 km
20. 2000 m = 2 km
21. 1500 m = 1·5 km
22. 10 000 m = 10 km

Page 100

Grams and kilograms

1. 1 kg = 1000 g
2. 2 kg = 2000 g
3. 7 kg = 7000 g
4. 10 kg = 10 000 g
5. 1$\frac{1}{2}$ kg = 1500 g
6. 5$\frac{1}{2}$ kg = 5500 g
7. 1 kg 600 g = 1600 g
8. 2 kg 420 g = 2420 g
9. 3 kg 560 g = 3560 g
10. 7 kg 180 g = 7180 g
11. 1100 g = 1 kg 100 g
12. 3000 g = 3 kg 0 g
13. 2600 g = 2 kg 600 g
14. 4300 g = 4 kg 300 g
15. 2150 g = 2 kg 150 g
16. 1850 g = 1 kg 850 g
17. 4635 g = 4 kg 635 g
18. 2742 g = 2 kg 742 g
19. 1803 g = 1 kg 803 g
20. 1045 g = 1 kg 45 g

Photocopy Masters

Litres and millilitres

1. 1000 ml = 1 l
2. 3000 ml = 3 l
3. 500 ml = 0·5 l
4. 7500 ml = 7·5 l
5. 1 l = 1000 ml
6. $\frac{1}{2}$ l = 500 ml
7. 2 l 300 ml = 2300 ml
8. $\frac{1}{10}$ l = 100 ml
9. 1 l = 2 pints
10. 2 l = 4 pints
11. 500 ml = 1 pint
12. 3500 ml = 7 pints
13. 2 pints = 1 l
14. 16 pints = 8 l
15. $\frac{1}{2}$ pint = $\frac{1}{4}$ l = 250 ml
16. 7 pints = $3\frac{1}{2}$ l

Area

1. 15 squares
2. 16 squares   largest area
3. 12 squares
4. 14 squares
5. 14 squares
6. 12 squares
7. 15 squares
8. 14 squares
9. 14 squares
10. 11 squares   smallest area

Area

1. 16 cm²
2. 14 cm²
3. 18 cm²
4. 12 cm²
5. 25 cm²
6. 28 cm²
7. 36 cm²
8. 35 cm²
9. 12 cm²
10. 12 cm²

Perimeter and area

	a	b	c	d	e	f	g	h	i	j	k
Perimeter cm	10	16	16	10	14	14	8	10	14	24	20
area cm²	6	16	15	4	8	10	4	4	10	36	25

Perimeter and area

Answers will vary.

Photocopy Masters

Page 106
Telling the time

1. 3:10	**2.** 4:15	**3.** 5:55	**4.** 3:26
5. 7:48	**6.** 9:31	**7.** 7:44	**8.** 2:52
9. 11:27	**10.** 6:03	**11.** 3:38	**12.** 10:09

Page 107
Telling the time

Page 108
Calendars

April

M	Tu	W	Th	F	Sa	Su
		1	2	3	4	5
6	7	8	9	10	11	12
13	14	15	16	17	18	19
20	21	22	23	24	25	26
27	28	29	30			

May

M	Tu	W	Th	F	Sa	Su
				1	2	3
4	5	6	7	8	9	10
11	12	13	14	15	16	17
18	19	20	21	22	23	24
25	26	27	28	29	30	31

Photocopy Masters

June						
M	Tu	W	Th	F	Sa	Su
1	2	3	4	5	6	7
8	9	10	11	12	13	14
15	16	17	18	19	20	21
22	23	24	25	26	27	28
29	30					

July						
M	Tu	W	Th	F	Sa	Su
		1	2	3	4	5
6	7	8	9	10	11	12
13	14	15	16	17	18	19
20	21	22	23	24	25	26
27	28	29	30	31		

Page 109
Time **M7**

Calendars
1. Sunday
2. Tuesday
3. Monday
4. Wednesday
5. Tuesday
6. Thursday
7. Tuesday
8. Sunday
9. Friday
10. Wednesday
11. Friday
12. Thursday
13. Thursday
14. Monday
15. Tuesday
16. Sunday

Page 110
Time **M8**

Timetable
1. 7 minutes
2. 18 minutes
3. 46 minutes
4. 68 minutes
5. 25 minutes
6. 55 minutes
7. 77 minutes
8. 61 minutes
9. 18 minutes
10. 22 minutes
11. 37 minutes
12. 22 minutes
13. 21 minutes
14. 43 minutes

Page 111
Time **M9**

Minutes and seconds
1. 65 seconds
2. 85 seconds
3. 120 seconds
4. 130 seconds
5. 185 seconds
6. 90 seconds
7. 150 seconds
8. 600 seconds
9. 1 minute 15 seconds
10. 1 minute 30 seconds
11. 1 minute 8 seconds
12. 1 minute 40 seconds
13. 2 minutes 0 seconds
14. 3 minutes 20 seconds

Photocopy Masters

Page 112
Polygons

1. rectangle
2. equilateral triangle
3. regular hexagon
4. pentagon
5. triangle
6. hexagon
7. pentagon
8. pentagon
9. hexagon

Page 113
Regular polygons

1. equilateral triangle
2. square
3. regular hexagon
4. regular octagon
5. regular heptagon
6. regular pentagon

Page 114
Isosceles triangles

1. **2.** **3.** **4.** **5.**

6. 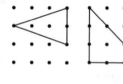 **7.** **8.** **q.**

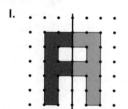

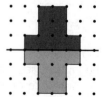

Page 115
Symmetry

1. **2.** **3.**

4.–q. Answers will vary.

Photocopy Masters

Page 122

Coordinates

1. (3,2)	**2.** (5,0)	**3.** (7,6)	**4.** (4,7)	**5.** (2,5)
6. (1,1)	**7.** (8,3)	**8.** (4,4)	**9.** (1,7)	**10.** (0,5)

Page 123

Frequency tables

digit	0	1	2	3	4	5	6	7	8	9
frequency	‖‖ = 3	⊬⊬ = 5	⊬⊬ ⊬⊬ ‖ = 11	⊬⊬ ‖‖‖ = 9	⊬⊬ ‖‖‖ = 8	⊬⊬ ⊬⊬ = 10	⊬⊬ ‖ = 6	⊬⊬ ‖‖‖ = 8	⊬⊬ ‖‖ = 7	⊬⊬ = 5

Page 124

Pictographs

1. 14 days	**2.** 16 days	**3.** 9 days	**4.** 19 days
5. July	**6.** May	**7.** 3 days	**8.** 5 days
9. 7 days	**10.** 5 days	**11.** 12 days	**12.** 16 days
13. 15 days	**14.** 22 days		

Page 125

Bar graphs

1. 30 children	**2.** 29 children	**3.** 26 children	**4.** 30 children
5. 29 children	**6.** 27 children	**7.** 24 children	**8.** 27 children
9. Y4	**10.** Y4	**11.** Y5	**12.** Y4
13. 5 children	**14.** 2 children	**15.** 5 children	**16.** 3 children

Page 126

Venn diagrams

1.

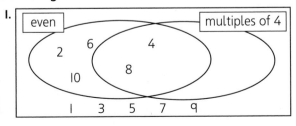

Photocopy Masters

Page 126 cont ...

2.

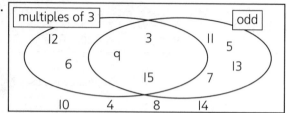

3.

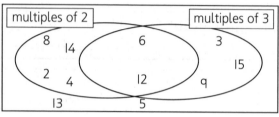

Page 127

Carroll diagrams

1.

	even	odd
multiple of 3	6 12	3 q
not a multiple of 3	8 2 4 10	1 7 5

2.

	factor of 4	not a factor of 4
multiple of 2	2 4	14 10 8 16 12 6 18
not a multiple of 2		q 13 15

3.

	digit total less than 10	digit total not less than 10
even	26 52 40	38 66 76 28
odd	15 17 63 45	77 85